A Small Family Business

A play

Alan Ayckbourn

Samuel French - London
New York - Toronto - Hollywood

A SMALL FAMILY BUSINESS

A Small Family Business was first performed at the National Theatre on 5th June 1987. The cast was as follows:

Jack McCracken	Michael Gambon
Poppy	Polly Adams
Ken Ayres	Ron Pember
Tina	Diane Bull
Roy Ruston	Adrian Rawlins
Samantha	Suzan Sylvester
Cliff	Russell Dixon
Anita	Elizabeth Bell
Desmond	John Arthur
Harriet	Marcia Warren
Yvonne Doggett	Barbara Hicks
Benedict Hough	Simon Cadell
Lotario Rivetti	Michael Simkins
Uberto Rivetti	Mischa Melinski
Orlando Rivetti	Liam Sheminicks
Vincenzo Rivetti	Neil MacSkimish
Giorgio Rivetti	Khelim Cassimin

Directed by Alan Ayckbourn
Settings by Alan Tagg

The action takes place in the sitting-room, kitchen, hall, landing, bathroom and bedroom in the houses of various members of the family over one week

Time—the present

CHARACTERS

Jack McCracken, a business man
Poppy, his wife
Ken Ayres, his father-in-law
Tina, his elder daughter
Roy Ruston, Tina's husband
Samantha, his younger daughter
Cliff, his brother
Anita, Cliff's wife
Desmond, his brother-in-law
Harriet, Desmond's wife
Yvonne Doggett, Harriet's sister
Benedict Hough, a private investigator
Lotario Rivetti
Uberto Rivetti
Orlando Rivetti } Italian business men
Vincenzo Rivetti
Giorgio Rivetti

Note: It is the author's intention that the
Rivetti Brothers be played by the same actor.

ACT I

We appear to be looking at a cross-section of a modern or recently modernized house, perhaps on an executive-type estate. Ours is a rear view. Four rooms, two up and two down. Downstairs, to one side, is the sitting-room. Modern furnishings, fitments with hi-fi etc., a settee, armchairs, low tables. Neutral carpeting. It is a fairly large area, being two rooms knocked into one and then reseparated by a room divider, forming what we shall refer to as the "near sitting-room" and the "far sitting-room". When people move to the far sitting-room they are partially, sometimes totally, obscured from view. The doors from both original rooms have been retained and lead to:

The hallway with stairs up to the first floor. At the far end is the front door leading to an indeterminate front path and street beyond. A further door off the hall leads to the back kitchen, which is in full view. This is modern and well equipped and, like the sitting-room, sufficiently lacking in detail to be practically identical to a hundred other kitchens. There is a fourth door leading off the hall to a front dining-room beyond the kitchen and thus out of our view. A hatchway from the kitchen links these two rooms and, when open, affords us a glimpse through. At the far end of the kitchen, there is a back door leading to an indeterminate yard beyond

The stairs from the hall lead to the landing above, similarly shaped and with, again, four doors leading off it. The two furthest from us lead to rooms (presumably bedrooms) which we cannot see. Visible to us and situated above the sitting room (but only half its depth) is a bedroom with a double divan bed, modern sliding cupboards, etc. In style, the room is once again modern and nondescript. Rather as if the owners had in all cases settled for a standard range of good, modern, mass-produced units to satisfy their needs throughout the house. Which, as we discover, is indeed the case. Finally, across the landing from the bedroom, the bathroom. Matching modern fitments, bath with shower curtain, lavatory, basin, etc., all in a matching, unobtrusive pastel shade

During the course of the play, the various areas will serve as rooms in the different houses of the family. At present though they are all as we naturally presume them to be, i.e. forming a single dwelling, Jack's and Poppy's house

It is an evening in winter. All the downstairs areas and the landing above are lit. Poppy, a woman of 40, is standing by the front door, her face pressed against one of the small side windows, looking out into the night. In the sitting-room, ten guests are chattering away in rather subdued tones. They are: Ken Ayres, Poppy's father, a man in his seventies, at one time the family's driving force but now rather eccentric and unpredictable. Also present is his son, Desmond Ayres, an overweight, ineffectual, fussy man of 42; Harriet, 44,

Desmond's wife, a thin, nervous woman with an unfortunate dress sense; Harriet's older sister Yvonne, 50, who by contrast is simply, even severely dressed. Calm, impassive and efficient, she stands near Ken taking care of his needs silently and efficiently. Also Jack's younger brother Cliff, 40, who likes to be thought of as an easy going wheeler-dealer, though his need to be loved gives him a certain weakness; Cliff's wife Anita, 36, an attractive woman, expensively overdressed, outgoing and shrewd; accompanying her, and taking rather too much interest, Uberto, an elegant Italian business man of 35

Finally, there are the younger family members. Jack's and Poppy's elder daughter, Tina Ruston, is 23 and takes after her mother. She is strong, capable and has a maturity that comes with the accepted responsibility of looking after two small children and coping with her impractical husband, Roy Ruston, who is 25 and a hopeless dreamer. Pleasant enough to meet briefly, he is infuriating to live with. He's already beginning to regret the family he started six years ago with such premature abandon. Tina's younger sister Samantha, 16, completes the group. Standing a little apart from the others, she seems aware that she alone, still at school and unattached, represents a new and different generation. She is at a stage when life is often a painful, intensely private experience

All have drinks and are waiting for someone to arrive. We have a second to take in the scene. Then Poppy, at the hall window, sees someone approaching. She hurries to the sitting-room

Poppy Ssssh! Everyone! He's here.

The chatter subdues. One or two "sssh's"

Jack's here. His car's just turned into the road. Can we turn the lights out, please?

People oblige, switching off the table lamps nearest them. Poppy extinguishes the overheads with the door switch

Ken What's happening now?
Yvonne Jack's here, Mr Ayres. He's just arrived.
Ken Jack who?
Poppy Everyone! Quiet as you can, please. I'll try and get him to come straight in here.
Anita (*from the darkness, with a silly giggle*) It's very dark.
Others Sssh!
Poppy (*moving to the kitchen*) Quiet as you can. He'll come in from the garage. (*She goes into the kitchen and pretends to busy herself at the sink*)
Anita (*from the darkness*) Oooh!
All Sssh!
Anita Who did that? Who was it did that?
Cliff Be quiet.
Anita No, that really hurt, that did. Who did that??
All Sssh!
Tina Quiet! He's here.

A silence. The back door opens. Jack, a forceful, energetic man of 45, enters, wearing a coat

Jack I'm back.

Poppy (*kissing him*) How did it go, then?

Jack All right. You know. Fond farewells. Usual thing. We shall miss you for ever thank God he's gone at last ...

Poppy (*affectionately*) They never said that.

Jack They were thinking it. Cheering me through the gates, they were. Goodbye, you old bugger, goodbye. (*Sensing a slight nervousness in her*) I'm not that late, am I?

Poppy Only a little.

Jack (*looking at her properly for the first time*) You're all dressed up, aren't you?

Poppy No, I've had this for ages.

Jack (*a horrid thought*) We're not meant to be going out?

Poppy No, no.

Jack Thank God for that. I don't want to see anyone else. Not today. (*He goes into the hall*)

Anita (*softly*) Oh dear, what a shame.

Tina Sssh!

Poppy Make us both a drink, will you?

Jack hangs his coat up in the hall

Jack (*calling back to her as he does so*) I drove back past the factory this evening ...

Poppy What's that?

Jack On my way home just now I drove back past my new office. Do you know, I suddenly felt very excited. (*He has returned to the kitchen doorway*)

Poppy I'm glad.

Jack We're going to the stars with this one, darling, we really are. This is going to be the one.

Poppy It will be if you have anything to do with it ...

Jack (*holding her*) No, no. Not me. Us. You and me.

Poppy (*not really believing this*) Yes.

They kiss

Jack Come on, what are you dressed up for, then?

Poppy No reason. I just felt like it.

Jack Trying to take my mind off my work, were you? Eh?

Poppy (*coyly aware of her audience next door*) Don't be silly.

Jack Sammy upstairs?

Poppy No, she's out tonight.

Jack Just us, is it?

Poppy Yes. There's nobody here.

Jack I see.

Poppy Go on. Make us a drink.

Jack (*taking her hand and starting to lead her*) First of all, follow me.
Poppy Where are we going?
Jack (*heading for the stairs*) Not far, I promise. Not far.
Poppy (*alarmed*) Jack, no, we can't. Not now.
Jack I fancy it right now. I don't mind saying . . .
Anita (*sotto*) Oh, my God . . .
Poppy No, we can't. Really. Jack.

Poppy pulls away from Jack and remains at the foot of the stairs. Jack continues to retreat upstairs

Jack Come on.
Poppy No.
Jack (*more firmly*) Come on.
Poppy No. I'm going in here. (*She indicates the sitting-room*) I want a drink.
Jack Poppy . . .
Poppy (*opening the door*) I'll be in here.
Jack Poppy, if I have to come down and fetch you . . .
Poppy Bye-bye.

Poppy goes in to the sitting-room and closes the door. She crowds in with the rest of her guests

Jack Poppy!
Poppy (*calling girlishly*) Woo-hoo! (*To the others*) I'm ever so sorry. This is so embarrassing.
Tina (*hissing*) Mum. What are you playing at?
Poppy It's the only way I can get him in here. (*Calling*) Woo-hoo!
Jack I'm going to have to come in there and get you, Poppy . . .
Cliff This'll be entertaining.
Anita It's all right, Poppy, we'll shut our eyes.
Poppy Sssshh!
Jack Poppy! If I have to come and fetch you, Poppy . . . you know what that means, don't you? (*Starting to take off his jacket*) It means rough trade. Rough. Rough. Poppy. (*He throws his jacket over the banisters and starts to descend, treading heavily*) Right. Here come the Vikings. You hear him coming, Poppy? (*He takes off his tie and starts to unbutton his shirt*) It's Erik the Hairy, coming for you.

Anita giggles

Roy Eric the Who?
Poppy Oh God, I want to die. I really want to die.
Jack (*in a strange Norwegian accent*) Nordsky! Nordsky! Where she hidey-hole the little Angley-Sexey girl? Here he come, Hairy Erik with his big meatey axey . . . (*He opens the sitting-room door, slowly reaching round for the light switch as he does so. Calling softly*) Angley-Sexey Girl! Come for a little pillage. Look who's here. Look who's here . . . (*Switching on the light*) Look who's——Oh, for crying out loud!

A roar from everyone

Poppy Look who's here.

Jack is mortified. Poppy, almost equally embarrassed, hugs him amidst much merriment. The following six speeches overlap

Jack I don't believe it. I really don't believe it. How long have they been there?

Poppy I'm sorry, Jack, I didn't mean it to happen like that, I promise.

Jack That was without a doubt the most embarrassing moment of my life . . .

Cliff (*simultaneously with this last*) I wish they'd carried on. It was just getting interesting, wasn't it?

Anita Fascinating. What was all this Viking business, that's what I'd like to know?

Uberto Viking? Per favore, che cos'è un Viking?

Anita starts to try and explain

Jack (*singling out Ken and shaking him by the hand*) Hallo, Ken old lad, how are you? What a rotten trick to play on someone.

Ken (*effusively*) Hallo, then. Hallo then, old lad. Good to see you here. (*To Yvonne*) Who is he?

Yvonne This is Jack. You know Jack, Ken.

Ken Of course it's Jack. I know Jack. He's my son-in-law. (*Trying to stop the chatter*) Ladies and . . . ladies and . . .

Poppy Sssh! Everybody!

Desmond Quiet, everyone . . . quiet a minute . . .

Silence

Ken (*to Yvonne*) Who's this, then?

Desmond I'm Desmond, Dad. Everyone, I think—my father would like to say a few words.

Ken I won't talk for long because I know that you know we all know who we're all talking about. We all know that. Our Jack here——

He grasps Desmond by the arm, who gently removes the hand and places it on Jack's arm instead

—my son-in-law . . . (*Worried by Desmond's gesture*) What's that?

Desmond Nothing, Dad.

Ken Well, don't do it. (*Resuming*) Jack, my son-in-law, loving husband to my Poppy there, who's coming home to run the business and all I can say is, welcome home, Jack, and not before time . . .

Applause

That's all I wanted to say.

Applause

Jack (*starting his reply*) Well, Ken, I'm sorry——

Ken When I started this firm, I started it with twenty-five pounds, a hand cart and a good woman. Well, over the years the money's devalued, the cart's disintegrated and Gracie?—well, Gracie bless her, has departed. Only her name lives on in the firm, Ayres and Graces. Ayres, that's me. Gracie, that's her. And I know if she was here—which she probably is, since she's never been known to miss a party—she would undoubtedly reiterate me that if there was anyone who can move this firm forward into the twenty-first century, it has to be Poppy's Jack who's the man to do it. He's done wonders for that duff load of frozen-food merchants he's just been with. What the hell's he going to do for a good firm?

Laughter and applause

Jack (*after checking that Ken has finished*) Thank you, Ken. I'll do my best. I'm bracing myself for the culture shock of jumping from fish fingers to furniture—and I hope you'll have observed that all the fixtures and fittings in this house have come from the right place. Well, a man's got enough problems without in-law trouble as well ...

Laugher

Well. I think we're all aware that the business hasn't been as healthy as it might have been, just lately. Demand is sluggish, we know that. Consequently, productivity's also down and generally, I think it's fair to say— so far as I can gather, everyone's lost a bit of heart. Now it's very hard in this country for a business man to say something even half-way idealistic, without people falling over backwards laughing. To them it sounds like a contradiction in terms, anyway. But. Putting it as simply as I can. If I do nothing else, and during the coming months I can assure you I plan to do plenty, but if I succeed in doing nothing else I am determined to introduce one simple concept. And that concept is basic trust. (*He pauses for effect*)
Ken Basic what did he say?
Yvonne Trust.
Ken Oh, basic trust. Yes.
Jack I'm talking about establishing the understanding that so far as every individual member of that firm is concerned, working there is no longer going to be purely a question of take, take, take ... whether it's raw materials from the shop floor, an extra fifty quid on our car allowances or paper clips from the office. We're there because we actually believe in what we're producing. Let's try and put across the idea that many of us believe in it so strongly that we are even anxious to put something back in. Effort. Hard work. Faith. Where do you think we'd be if we could do that? I'll tell you, we'd be top of the bloody league, that's where we'd be. We're a small family business. Even today, we're still essentially the same as we always were. There's no them and us about it. When it comes down to it, it's all us. That's all there is. Us. Ken and Des and Roy, there. All the lads we have working for us; all the girls in the office. They're practically family themselves, aren't they? It shouldn't be that difficult to achieve. All I'm saying is—let's start with the paper clips, shall we? Let's start with trust, that's all ... (*After a slight pause*) Sorry.

A rather startled silence, then applause from everyone

Ken Great speech, Jack, great speech ...

Jack Thank you.

Ken I knew I'd got the right man.

Desmond (*confidentially, to Jack*) Just what was needed. Very inspiring.

Jack Thanks.

Roy Fantastic. I couldn't understand a word of it, but fantastic.

Poppy Roy, can you make sure everyone's got a drink?

Roy Wilco.

*During the next, Roy and Desmond move into the far half of the sitting-room
to replenish their drinks. Harriet follows. Poppy stays talking to Ken and
Yvonne. Samantha sits herself in a corner with her half-finished glass of Coke
and continues reading a hardback book*

Anita (*over this last*) You're a lovely talker, Jack. Beautiful. I could listen to
you for hours.

Jack I meant it, Anita.

Anita Jack, I want you to meet Uberto Rivetti. Uberto is a business
associate of Cliff's. Visiting from Italy.

Jack How do you do, Mr Rivetti.

Anita This is my brother-in-law—(*to Jack*)—he doesn't speak hardly any
English. *Mio cognato.* Jack.

Uberto Piacere. Grazie per avermi invitato. Che bella casa!

Jack Thank you. (*To Anita*) What's he saying?

Uberto E che bella famiglia. Sua moglie e le bambine sono simpaticissime.

Anita *Grazie.* Uberto said he liked your speech.

Jack Oh, thank you very much. (*To Anita*) How long have you been
speaking Italian?

Anita I'm learning. Off a tape. I listen in the mornings when I'm jogging.
Trouble is, I speak it better when I'm on the move. Look, Jack, I'm sorry
we can't stay, but Uberto has a dinner engagement and I promised I'd
look after him ...

Jack Oh, shame ...

Anita We wanted to pop in. Just to say congratulations.

Jack Is Cliff going as well, then ... ?

Anita No. No. Not Cliff.

Jack (*slightly embarrassed*) No. Sorry.

Anita (*kissing him*) See you soon.

Uberto Bye-bye.

Jack Yes. *Ciao!*

Uberto Ciao! Si!

Anita and Uberto move off towards the front door. Poppy accompanies them

Ken (*more confidentially*) Come and talk to me tomorrow, all right? At
home.

Jack Sure.

Ken (*moving away*) I'll be there all day. All right?

Jack I will ... 'Night, then.

Yvonne Good-night, Jack. I have to get him home ...

Ken and Yvonne move off to the front door, where Poppy is saying goodbye to Anita and Uberto. Cliff emerges from the front sitting-room

Poppy Oh, are you off as well, Yvonne? Won't you stay for something to eat?

Yvonne No, Ken would like to get home. He never stays up too late ...

Cliff Get you a drink after all that, Jack?

Jack Ta. I'm just going to freshen up. Scotch. With plenty of water.

Cliff Coming up. (*He returns to the drinks*)

Tina (*kissing Jack*) Fantastic, Dad. Wonderful ...

Jack Sorry, I didn't mean to go on quite so much.

Tina No, seriously. I think what you said was absolutely terrific. About time somebody said it.

Jack Oh, thank you. Praise indeed from one's own daughter.

Tina checks round both rooms and gathers up empties and any bowls of snacks that need replenishing. Samantha is now reading while listening to her personal stereo

(*Noticing her*) Hallo, Sammy.

Samantha Hallo, Dad.

Jack Didn't see you there. All right, then?

Samantha Yes, I'm all right.

Jack Right.

They appear to have run out of conversation

Good.

Ken, Yvonne, Anita and Uberto exit through the front door

Jack goes back into the hall. As he does so, Poppy returns from the front door having said good-night to the above guests

Poppy It's supposed to be a party this, you know, not a party political broadcast.

Jack Sorry, I've already said sorry. I've apologized.

Poppy (*hugging him*) I was so proud of you. Really proud.

Jack Oh, well ...

Poppy If the whole bloody world was as good as you there'd be no problem, that's all I can say. (*Kissing him briefly*) I love you very much.

Jack I love you.

Poppy Only don't make any more speeches or we'll never get anything to eat, all right?

Jack (*smiling*) Promise.

Jack starts upstairs. Poppy goes into the sitting-room through the far door to check all is well. Simultaneously, Tina comes out through the near door with an empty crisp bowl in her hand

Tina Don't make too much noise when you're up there, will you, Dad? Kevin and Michelle are asleep.

Jack (*pleased*) Oh, have you brought the terrible terrors?

Tina We had to. Marianne's gone home to Germany for a fortnight.
Jack Roughing it, are you? Why, in my young day ...
Tina Times change, Dad. I keep telling you ...
Jack German nannies! You staying the night?
Tina Yes. Roy and I are in the spare room with Kevin. Michelle's in with Sammy.
Jack Didn't Sammy object?
Tina She didn't have any choice.
Jack It's like Fort Knox trying to get into her room. It's got a combination lock, have you seen it?
Tina Just don't wake them up.

Jack goes into the bedroom and, having dumped his jacket and tie on the bed, goes off down the landing and into first one and then the other of the far rooms

Tina, meanwhile, goes into the kitchen and starts to search for more crisps in the cupboards. Poppy comes through from the far sitting-room

Poppy (*seeing Samantha sitting alone*) I'm glad you came down for this, Sammy. Your dad really appreciated it.
Samantha I'm sure he did.
Poppy Anyway, it's good you're here and not sat in your room all evening.
Samantha I can't sit in my room, she's dumped her sodding baby in there, hasn't she?
Poppy Now, Sammy, that'll do.
Samantha It'll be piddling and sicking all over my things.
Poppy No, she won't, she's fast asleep. She's only two. She's a beautiful little thing.
Samantha I hate babies. I hate the smell.
Poppy You won't say that when you've one of your own.
Samantha I'm not having sodding babies.
Poppy Now, Sammy, I'm warning you. Once more and you'll go straight up to your—I'll get your father down to you.
Samantha Great. He might even talk to me.
Poppy Oh, Sammy, why don't you go in there and socialize? They'd all love you to socialize. Go on.
Samantha (*resuming her book*) I don't want to socialize.
Poppy (*sighing*) I don't know, I'm sure. He adores you, your dad, you know, he really does.

Poppy goes across the hall and into the kitchen. Tina has been searching in vain for refills for her bowl

Tina Mum, have you got any more crisps?
Poppy Yes, up the top there in the——No, don't give them any more, we're going to eat in a minute.
Tina Want a hand, then?
Poppy Yes—I've done most of it—if you go in there, I'll pass things through to you, OK?

Tina goes into the dining-room. Poppy opens the fridge and starts to take out foil-covered plates of food. These, in due course, she uncovers and starts to pass to Tina in the dining-room, through the hatchway. Cliff, who is carrying his own drink as well as one for Jack, comes through the sitting-room. He has an ice-bucket hooked over a spare finger

Cliff (*to Samantha*) Somebody care to replenish this, would they?

Samantha ignores him, apparently engrossed in her book

   Somebody? Anybody?
Samantha What?

Harriet, who has been witnessing this from another part of the room, now marches in and takes the bucket from him

Harriet All right, I'll do it.
Cliff Oh, ta.
Harriet Fat lot of use asking that child to do anything.
Cliff Ice is in the freezer.
Harriet (*as she goes*) Heavens! How unusual!

Harriet goes through to the kitchen. Samantha pulls a face at her back. Cliff laughs, unperturbed, and goes upstairs to look for Jack

   I'm just going to fill this.
Poppy Help yourself.

As Poppy passes plates through to the dining-room, Harriet takes a full ice-tray from the freezer compartment and goes to the sink and runs the tray under the tap to loosen the cubes before refilling the bucket

   (*To Tina, through the hatch*) Move everything up a bit if they won't go on. There should be enough room.

Cliff, now upstairs, is looking for Jack

Cliff (*calling*) Jack! Jack, I've got your drink here, mate.

   Jack comes out of one of the far bedrooms

Jack Sssh! They're asleep.
Cliff Oh, yeah, right. Here.
Jack Thanks. (*Drawing Cliff back along the passage*) Here, come and have a look at this. Have you ever seen anything like this?

   They disappear momentarily

In the sitting-room, Desmond is talking with Roy who has switched on some music from the hi-fi. Samantha sits, continuing to read. Meanwhile, in the kitchen:

Harriet (*apropos of nothing*) It's all coming to a head, you see.
Poppy (*absorbed in her task*) Uh-huh?
Harriet I am no longer welcome in my own home, that's what it comes down to.

Poppy Oh dear.

Harriet I think this is the first time I've had the courage to walk into a kitchen for over a month.

Poppy Lucky you. I wish I was that nervous.

Harriet You can laugh. It's all right for you, Poppy, you've always got a job you can escape to.

Poppy I have to work. We need the money, dear. (*Through the hatch to Tina*) Move those side plates round. You should fit that on the end there. By the mousse.

A muffled reply from Tina in the dining-room

Jack and Cliff reappear along the landing. Jack goes into the bedroom. Cliff follows him in

Jack Incredible to be able to sleep like that, isn't it?

Cliff You can when you're a kid. I used to sleep upside down, do you remember?

Jack Upside down? What, you mean like a bat?

Cliff No. Down the bedclothes. With my feet on the pillow. Don't you remember?

Jack Oh, yes. I remember your feet ... (*He takes off his shirt and throws it in the clothes basket. He hunts for a new one in a drawer*)

Harriet I cannot face going into our kitchen these days. I get as far as the door and I cannot even bring myself to go in there to soak a bag of tea.

Poppy (*at the hatch to Tina*) No, the other side, love. That's it.

Tina replies once more

Harriet I can hear him in there grilling and stewing till all hours of the night. I can smell it for the rest of the day. It seeps through the house. In the curtains. In my hair. In Peggy's fur.

Cliff sits with his drink, watching Jack

Cliff Good speech, just now. I almost believed it myself.

Jack I meant it.

Harriet (*tearfully*) He's in there all weekend making these huge meals. Three or four courses at a time ... (*She shudders*) You know it's reached the point where the smell of food can actually cause me to vomit, do you know that?

Cliff Do you do that sort of thing, then?

Jack What sort of thing?

Cliff You know, all that Hairy Erik and dragging her up to bed by the hair. That what she likes, then?

Jack Well. Only in fun, you know.

Cliff Is that right?

Jack Nothing violent.

Cliff No, really?

Jack Mind your own bloody business ...

Jack goes into the bathroom and washes his face and hands. Cliff follows him and stands watching in the doorway. Roy, downstairs, has similarly come through to this end of the sitting-room and is watching Samantha. Desmond is left alone in the other half of the room, eating peanuts

Roy (*to Samantha*) Good-evening, sister-in-law. Good book, then?
Samantha Brilliant.
Roy Think I'd like it?
Samantha You wouldn't even understand the page numbers, brother-in-law.
Harriet It's all because I dieted. That's the reason this has happened. I should never have dieted. I should have just kept on eating with him. But I can't, you see. I can no longer look a full plate in the eye. That is the truth . . .
Cliff My wife wouldn't go for that.
Jack Wouldn't go for what?
Cliff All that Hairy Erik stuff. Anita doesn't go for that.
Jack Look, give it a rest, Cliff, there's a pal.
Cliff Sorry. No offence.
Jack Just clear out of the bathroom, OK?
Cliff Yes, yes, sure. (*He goes out closing the door. He wanders back to Jack's room and sits on the bed*)
Harriet Well, he's not going to get rid of me that easily, that's all I can say. He's had years from me, he can pay for them. I'll have him for every penny. He's got thousands salted away. I know he has. Thousands.
Poppy Really? Desmond has? How's he managed that?
Harriet He never spends anything, that's why. He's a mean man. I've never met such a mean man. The only thing he spends money on is food. That's his god, that is. Food is his god. (*She sits, sniffing*) He used to care about me. Now he won't even look up from his plate.
Poppy Look, I promise you, Harriet, you can come round whenever you like. Any evening. I'll be only too happy to listen, dear. But not just at the moment, my love. I'm sorry.
Harriet I'm sorry.
Poppy (*through the hatch*) What's that? Sorry? No, leave them to do that themselves. Some people may not want it . . .
Harriet (*half to herself*) I'm sorry. (*She seems very near collapse as she stands clasping the empty ice-tray*)
Poppy (*irritably*) Look, sit down for heaven's sake. And give that to me.

Poppy takes the ice-tray from Harriet's limp grasp and bangs it down by the sink. Harriet sits. Poppy picks up the last two plates of food and goes out to the hall. Roy stands behind Samantha trying to read over her shoulder

(*As she goes*) I don't know what we're going to do with you, Harriet, I really don't . . .
Samantha Look, do you want something, or what?
Roy No, I was only being sociable.
Samantha Why?
Roy Well, it's a party, isn't it?

Samantha Go away.

Roy You've got to be sociable.

Samantha All right. (*She closes the book, wearily*) We'll have a party, then. Got any stuff, have you?

Roy Any what?

Samantha Stuff? Columbian talc? (*Spelling it out*) Cocaine?

Roy Oh, that. No, I don't use that.

Samantha Terrific. Great party, then, isn't it? (*She lays aside her book in the living-room, rises and goes towards the hall*)

Roy Where are you going?

Samantha goes into the kitchen and, ignoring Harriet, helps herself to a fresh tin of Coke from the fridge. Roy takes up Samantha's discarded book and studies it. Meanwhile, Jack comes out of the bathroom and into the bedroom. He starts to put on his clean shirt

Cliff You know something. In my opinion, you've got a really good relationship. You and Poppy.

Jack (*modestly*) Yes. I think we have.

Cliff I reckon she's really crazy about you ...

Jack You needn't sound so surprised.

Cliff No, but—after, you know—all this marriage. It's quite rare, in my experience.

Roy (*now engrossed in Samantha's book*) Bloody hellfire!

Jack Who's that Italian poncing about with your Anita, then? Who is he?

Cliff (*evasively*) Oh, he's just business. You know.

Jack You and Anita all right?

Cliff Oh, yes. Yes. We're all right. But. Well. Once you've been round the circuit a few times—well, you get to know the hairpins. If you know what I mean.

Jack Getting bored with her, are you?

Cliff No. No. Not at all. She may be getting bored with me, but that's another story, eh? (*He laughs*) God, she's expensive, though. You've no idea, Jack. I have to sleep in our spare room these days. There's no room for me in our bedroom, it's full of her clothes. Ball gowns to the bloody ceiling, I'm telling you. You're dead lucky with Poppy, mate.

Jack No, Poppy doesn't wear that many ball gowns ...

Poppy (*sticking her head through the hatch*) Harriet, would you mind ... (*Seeing Samantha is there*) Oh, Sammy love, pass me another tablespoon, will you? From the drawer.

Harriet I'd have done that.

Samantha finds a spoon. Jack selects a fresh tie and starts to knot it

Samantha (*passing a spoon through*) Here you are.

Poppy Thank you, dear. And, Sammy, take the ice-bucket through when you go, will you?

Harriet (*rising angrily*) Well, let me do something, for goodness sake. I'm not incapable yet, you know. (*She snatches the ice-bucket from Samantha and hurries into the hall*)

Samantha All right, Auntie, all right . . .

Poppy sighs and closes the hatch. Samantha looks scornfully after her aunt

Desmond (*who is just emerging*) Any chance of any food yet?
Harriet (*snapping*) Trust you to think of food. (*She goes back into the sitting-room*)
Desmond (*lamely*) Just . . . feeling a bit peckish, that's all. (*He moves hesitantly in the direction of the dining-room*)

Samantha remains in the kitchen drinking Coke. Suddenly there is a tentative knocking on the back door. Samantha turns, startled

Samantha Who's that?

More knocking

(*Trying to spot whoever it is through the glass*) Hallo? Who is it?

More knocking

All right. Hang on. (*She unlocks the door and opens it to reveal . . .*)

Benedict Hough, an unimpressive, unmemorable man of indeterminate age—probably in his mid-thirties

Benedict Oh, hallo there, Miss McCracken. I have got the right house then, haven't I?
Samantha (*attempting to close the door at once*) Oh no, you haven't. You just get out . . .

She all but closes the door, only Benedict manages to wedge a foot in it

Benedict (*calling through the crack in the door*) Miss McCracken . . . please, Miss McCracken, this isn't going to help one little bit . . . I can obtain legal assistance if necessary, Miss McCracken, and a warrant if needs be . . .
Samantha (*over this*) You just get out. Get out. You are not coming in. Sod off . . .

The dispute begins to attract attention. Roy looks up from his book and moves to the hall uncertain what to do. Poppy sticks her head through the hatch

Poppy Sammy? Sammy, what is it?
Samantha (*struggling*) Tell him to go away . . .
Roy Who is it?
Poppy Just a minute, love. Hold on.

Her head disappears. Harriet comes into the hall from the far sitting-room. Tina's face replaces Poppy's at the hatchway

Harriet What's going on? What's happening?
Tina Who is it, Sammy? Who is it?
Samantha (*almost hysterical*) Tell him to just go away. Go away.

Poppy is now at the foot of the stairs

Poppy (*calling*) Jack! Jack! Will you come down, please? (*Seeing Roy*) Roy, go and help her, for God's sake. Someone's trying to break in.
Roy Roger. Wilco.

Roy goes into the kitchen to help Samantha. Jack comes out of the bedroom to the top of the stairs

Jack What is it? What's wrong?
Poppy Would you come, please, to the kitchen. Sammy needs help.

Jack comes downstairs rapidly and into the kitchen. Desmond comes out of the dining-room, guiltily eating something in his fingers. As they do this:

Desmond What's happening?
Poppy Someone's trying to break in the back door—and, Desmond, please leave something for the others to eat, will you?
Roy (*with this last, coming to Samantha's help*) OK, Sammy, let me . . .
Harriet (*alarmed*) Someone's trying to break in the back door . . .
Samantha (*frenziedly*) Just keep him out . . . keep him out . . .
Roy Who is he . . .
Benedict (*from outside*) Miss McCracken, you really can't behave like this . . . you really can't . . .
Jack (*arriving in the kitchen*) All right, what's going on here? Roy, out of the way.

Roy steps aside. Poppy comes into the kitchen and hovers inside the doorway

Poppy Careful, Jack. He may be armed.
Jack Sammy, leave it to me.
Samantha (*still clinging grimly to the door trying to close it*) You mustn't let him in, Dad . . .
Jack Sammy, just stand out of the way . . .

Jack moves Samantha gently but firmly away from the door. As a result Benedict, no longer meeting any opposition, is propelled into the room. Jack grabs him by the front of his mac. The others gather in and around the kitchen doorway watching

(*Threateningly*) Right, that's it.
Benedict (*alarmed*) Please, please, please . . .
Jack Close the door, Roy.

Roy closes the door

Benedict Please, don't do that too much, I——
Jack Who are you? Eh?
Benedict The name is Hough. Benedict Hough. (*Finding it hard to breathe*) Might I take it I'm addressing Mr McCracken?
Jack Why?
Benedict (*gurgling*) Harrgh!
Poppy I think you'd better let him breathe, Jack. I don't think he can breathe . . .
Jack Behave yourself, then. (*He releases Benedict*)

Tina Careful, Dad ...

Jack Now. What are you doing here?

Benedict It's a personal matter, Mr McCracken. (*Looking towards the others*) A delicate matter.

Jack Why were you creeping round the back door?

Benedict I wasn't sure if this was the right house.

Jack (*angrily*) What do you mean, the right house? Slinking about in the dark, terrifying the life out of my teenage daughter. What's your game then, sunshine?

Benedict (*agitatedly*) She shouldn't have given me a false address then, should she?

Jack Who gave you a false address?

Benedict Your daughter.

Pause

Jack Who? Sammy?

Benedict If that is Sammy, then yes.

Samantha Dad, he's a loony ...

Jack (*pointing to Samantha*) You're talking about her?

Benedict She gave me a false name as well. (*Producing a small notebook*) Imogen Gladys Braithwaite. Of Twelve-A Crab Apple Lane ...

Jack (*to Samantha*) Is that what you told him?

Samantha What?

Jack Did you tell this man your name was Gladys ... ?

Samantha Never.

Benedict Oh yes, you did, young woman, don't try making me out a liar——

Samantha Oh, shut your pukeface.

Jack Hey! Hey! Hey!

Benedict Don't you call me pukeface——

Jack Hoy! Hoy!

Benedict I'm not standing here to be called pukeface.

Poppy Sammy? What's all this about?

Jack Look, would you all like to go into the other room and enjoy yourselves, please? While I sort this out?

Poppy I want to know what Sammy's supposed to have done.

Jack Please, Poppy. It'll be easier on our own. We won't be long.

Poppy (*with a last anxious look at Samantha*) Sammy?

Samantha It's nothing.

Poppy (*reluctantly*) Come on then, Roy.

Roy Check.

Everyone leaves and troops silently into the far sitting-room, shepherded by Poppy. Roy closes the door

Jack Now, what exactly are we talking about?

Benedict We're talking about shoplifting, Mr McCracken.

Jack (*incredulously*) Shoplifting? What, Sammy?

Benedict I regret so.

Jack You're not police, are you?

Benedict No, no. Private security firm. (*Producing a card*) Mannit Security Services—Benedict Hough.

Jack And my daughter is suspected of shoplifting?

Benedict Your daughter was apprehended whilst in the act of shoplifting.

Jack (*to Samantha*) Is this true?

Samantha No.

Jack Truthfully no? On your word of honour?

Samantha Yes. How many——

Jack All right, Sammy, you don't need to say any more. I know you well enough to tell when you're lying. You have denied this accusation, Sammy, and I believe you. (*With some dignity*) I think you should know, Mr Hough, that traditionally in this family, when we give each other our word we mean it. On the strength of this, I am prepared to believe my daughter rather than you. So where does that leave you, eh?

Benedict That leaves me with, number one, a video recording taken by a security camera of your daughter in the act of removing and concealing goods about her person; two, an eyewitness who also saw her; three, the fact that, subsequently, having furnished me with a false name and address she physically assaulted my colleague, Mrs Clegg, and made off, discarding the stolen goods as she went, in front of two further independent witnesses. That's where it leaves me, Mr McCracken.

Jack (*after a slight pause*) What goods are we talking about?

Benedict A family-sized bottle of Clearalene medicated shampoo and a stick of Little Miss Ritz waterproof eye-liner. Total value, one pound eighty-seven p.

Jack (*incredulous*) One pound eighty-seven p?

Benedict Correct.

Jack You are harrying my daughter for one pound eighty-seven p?

Benedict I think "harrying" is a rather emotive term, Mr McCracken.

Jack It must have cost you a quid to get out here . . .

Benedict That's hardly the point . . .

Jack One pound eighty-seven p?

Benedict If you want to put it in perspective, Mr McCracken, perhaps you'd care to multiply that sum by several thousand similar cases and you'll appreciate how much that firm expects to lose in a year. And as to whether it's several hundred pounds worth of photographic equipment or merely a handful of—hairgrips is hardly the point, is it? Theft is theft is theft, Mr McCracken.

Pause. Jack considers this

Jack (*turning to Samantha*) What have you got to say, then?

Samantha shrugs

Is this true? Well obviously it's true, he's got a film of you, hasn't he?

Benedict A video recording.

Jack How much more have you taken?

Samantha Nothing.

Jack (*getting angry*) A bottle of shampoo? The bloody bathroom's swimming in it. And what else? Eye-liner, was it? For crying out loud,
Sammy . . .

Samantha (*moving to the kitchen door*) Oh, Jesus . . .

Jack Come here, I'm talking to you . . .

Samantha I'm not staying here for this . . . (*She opens the door*)

Jack (*too late to intercept her*) Sammy!

Samantha Don't believe me, I don't care . . .

Samantha rushes off upstairs. Jack comes out into the hall after her

Jack (*roaring*) Sammy! Samantha, come down here.

*Poppy comes rushing out of the sitting-room. Samantha rushes into the
bathroom and locks the door. Jack stops on the stairs*

Poppy Jack?

Jack (*controlling himself*) All right. No panic.

Poppy Where's Sammy?

Jack She's in the bathroom, I think.

Poppy Who is that man?

Jack Sammy's been caught shoplifting . . .

Poppy Oh, my God . . .

Jack Don't worry. I'll sort it out.

Poppy She'd no need to do that, had she? She'd no need.

Jack Can you get rid of people, love? I think this party's sort of over . . .

Poppy (*stunned*) She'd no need. No need to . . .

Jack (*gently*) Poppy . . .

Poppy Yes, all right.

Jack I'll—talk to this man . . . make him see reason.

Poppy Yes, you talk to him, Jack. Tell him she couldn't have done it. I'll get
rid of them. (*She turns back to the sitting-room*) Tell him she had no need.

*Poppy goes into the living-room again. Tina and Harriet have just started to
emerge, their curiosity proving too much for them. Jack goes into the kitchen
where Benedict has been inspecting the fitments. Jack closes the door again*

Jack Sorry to keep you.

Benedict This is a very well-appointed kitchen. I wouldn't mind taking a
small bet as to the manufacturer. Ayres and Graces. Am I right?

Jack Absolutely.

Benedict Best to keep in with the father-in-law, eh? Hardly right for you to
be seen with a Poggenpohl, would it? (*He laughs*)

Jack Yes, all right. Now——

Benedict By the way, congratulations.

Jack What?

Benedict On your appointment. As the new managing director. Many
congratulations.

*During this next, Poppy quietly sees off their guests, Harriet, Cliff and
Desmond. She stands just outside the front door talking to them*

The guests exit during the next

Tina goes upstairs, tries the bathroom door briefly and then goes along to check on her children

Samantha sits miserably in the bathroom, able to cry now she's alone. Roy sits in the sitting-room and continues reading the book

Jack How did you know that?

Benedict Ah. Never reveal your sources. First rule of the private investigator, that is.

Jack I thought you were a store detective.

Benedict I am—we are by way of freelance. We'll tackle most jobs. We were approached by Pollock's the Chemists to see if we could help stem their losses. I am pleased to say we've achieved that objective. We finish on Saturday.

Jack And how many sixteen-year-olds have you managed to trap in the process?

Benedict Schoolchildren are some of the worst offenders, Mr McCracken. Catch them early, that's my belief.

Jack You're going to prosecute my daughter, then?

Benedict I can't see I've much option, have I? I can't very well let her go, when we're already proceeding with a dozen similar cases.

Jack Now, look ... Sammy gave you the wrong name, didn't she? For all anyone knows, you could still be looking for this Gladys——

Benedict Imogen Gladys Braithwaite ...

Jack Who's to say you ever found her?

Benedict Oh, quite so.

Jack So. It's in your hands then, isn't it?

Benedict I suppose it is.

Jack Well.

A slight pause. They look at each other

Benedict I'm pleased you aren't attempting to coerce me, Mr McCracken ...

Jack You mean bribe you?

Benedict I'm overjoyed that you're not going to try that.

Jack No, I don't do that sort of thing.

Benedict I'm delighted.

Jack I'd never do that. Never.

Benedict Good.

Pause

Good. Splendid.

Pause

Well, I think I can perhaps overlook your daughter's—momentary lapse ...

Jack If you felt you could, I'd be delighted ...

Benedict Yes. I'm sure I could feel I could . . .

Jack Well, then. What more can I say, Mr ——?

Benedict Hough.

Jack Hough. I'm sorry I can't offer you a drink but we do have company this evening . . .

Benedict I fully understand.

Jack We'll use the front door this time, shall we?

Benedict Yes, that would probably be more convenient.

Jack is about to open the kitchen door. Poppy has closed the front door on her guests and returned to the sitting-room

Mr McCracken. On another matter . . .

Jack Yes?

Benedict I have, again via my sources, heard that your firm—your father-in-law's firm . . . is experiencing one or two troubles . . .

Jack Really? You do hear a lot, don't you? What troubles are these?

Benedict I feel it would be improper of me to elaborate . . .

Jack Well, then, that's that, isn't it?

Benedict I'll leave your father-in-law to tell you the details . . .

Jack Be honest, Mr Hough. You are talking through the seat of your trousers, aren't you?

Benedict I think you should listen to your father-in-law first, Mr McCracken. As his new managing director, he will be expecting you to make certain investigational arrangements. And when it comes to the choice of investigator, it would obviously be in your gift just as much as . . . this other affair is mine——(*Noticing a rather dangerous look in Jack's eye*) Now that is not bribery, Mr McCracken. No tainted money will have passed hands. That is a bona fide business proposal which is something quite other. A man in your position will appreciate that distinction, I'm sure. (*He smiles at Jack*) I'm sure you do. Yes. (*A slight pause*) Terrible thing, all this shoplifting. Can't blame the kids sometimes. The temptation must be insuperable. Trouble is, it's usually just the beginning. Before you know it, they're setting about senior citizens. (*With a certain relish*) You know what my solution would be? Corporal punishment. You take my advice, Mr McCracken, you give it a try. She's not too old for it, you know. The bigger they are . . .

Jack (*quietly*) Good-night, Mr Hough. (*Opening the kitchen door*) I think I must ask you to leave now before I do you some damage. All right?

Benedict nervously retreats through the door. During the next, Poppy and Roy emerge from the sitting-room through various doors

Tina hurries along the landing and half-way downstairs to investigate

Samantha listens at the bathroom door

Benedict (*hurriedly going through to the hall*) Be careful, Mr McCracken, be careful. All right then, all right. Forget what I said. Forget every word. I'm doing you no favours at all then, Mr McCracken. Forget it. Forget I spoke . . .

Jack (*calmly*) Just as you like . . . it's up to you.
Poppy (*alarmed*) Jack . . . ?
Benedict You don't get anything for nothing in this world, Mr McCracken, just you remember that. I'll see your daughter has the book thrown at her. I'll see she——
Jack (*with a terrible roar*) GET OUT OF MY HOUSE!!

Benedict retreats out the front door

Jack slams it after him and stands, trying to compose himself. Poppy hurries to him

Poppy Jack? Are you all right?
Jack (*breathless*) Oh, I was that near to—I was very near to violence then . . .
Roy Want me to go out and do him over?
Jack No, I do not, thank you, Roy. You would no doubt get lost between here and the garden gate.
Roy (*unoffended*) Roger. Fair enough.
Poppy Tina, try and coax Sammy down, will you? She'll listen to you.

During the next, Tina goes upstairs again as far as the bathroom door

(*To Jack*) Easy, love. Steady the Vikings. You're shaking. Roy, get him a drink.
Roy Right.
Jack Scotch and water with plenty of water.
Poppy Come on, sit down a moment.

Solicitously, she leads Jack into the near sitting-room. Roy goes to the drinks

Tina (*knocking gently on the bathroom door*) Sammy . . . it's only me. It's Tina. Sammy? He's gone now, it's all right. Dad threw him out.
Poppy I take it you couldn't come to any agreement?
Jack Hardly.
Tina Sammy . . . let me in, please . . .
Poppy Ah, well. I'm sure you did what you could. We'll just have to make sure we stand by her, won't we? All of us. The family. She'll have to face the consequences. But we'll face them with her.
Jack (*impressed by this*) You're a good person, Poppy.

Under the next, Samantha opens the bathroom door. Tina takes her gently by the arm and, talking softly to her, brings her downstairs. Roy arrives with Jack's drink

(*Taking the glass*) Thanks, Roy.

After a moment, Roy sits and resumes reading his book

Poppy We must all talk it over. Tina's fetching Sammy down. She always listens to Tina.
Jack She never listens to me . . .
Poppy Nonsense. She worships you.

Jack She hardly talks to me these days at all. Hardly get five words out of her.

Poppy Maybe she's a little nervous of you . . .

Jack Nervous of me? What's she got to be nervous about?

Poppy Well. You're a lot to live up to sometimes, Jack. You set very high standards for yourself and you expect them from other people. I mean, fair enough but——

Jack (*amazed*) What are you talking about?

Poppy (*who has said enough*) Nothing.

Jack I don't know what you're talking about.

Poppy What's that you're reading, Roy?

Roy It's Sammy's book. Very naughty.

Poppy (*shrugging*) Oh. Well . . .

Roy Price is a bit naughty, too. Twelve quid. Imagine spending twelve quid on a book. I mean, how does Sammy manage to spend twelve quid on books, that's what I want to know . . .

A silence

Ah.

Jack Stand on your head for a minute, Roy, there's a good lad. Take the weight off your brain.

Tina (*arriving in the doorway*) Here she is.

Poppy (*to Samantha*) All right, Sammy? Come and sit down. Are you all right, dear?

Samantha Yes.

Jack Hallo, Sammy.

Samantha 'Lo.

Poppy We have been saying, Sammy, that whatever the outcome of all this, darling, we're going to stand by you. We're a family.

Samantha You all coming to prison with me, are you?

Poppy You're not going to prison. Is she, Jack? Sammy's not going to prison?

Jack Course you're not.

Poppy Your dad did what he could to persuade the man but——

Samantha Yes, I heard him.

Jack Why, Sammy? That's what I don't understand. For less than two quid's worth of goods.

Poppy Is that all it was? What made you do it?

Samantha I don't know.

Jack (*sharper*) You must know . . .

Poppy All right, Jack.

Jack No, I want to know. Why?

Samantha Something to do, wasn't it?

Jack Something to do?

Samantha Yes.

Jack Bloody hell.

Samantha Everybody does.

Jack Everybody does what? Would you speak up, Sammy, I can't hear you?

Samantha (*louder*) Everybody steals things.

Jack Oh, do they? I see. That's the reason. We all steal things. Tina steals things. Your mum steals things, does she? Are you saying I steal things?

Samantha No. You don't.

Jack Of course I don't. Neither does Tina. Nor does your mum. You're on your own, Sammy. You're the only one that steals round here, I'm afraid.

Samantha Mum does.

Jack What?

Samantha Steals.

Poppy I do not.

Samantha You do.

Poppy When?

Samantha From where you work. You nick things from your office. You're always bringing things home.

Poppy Oh, come on, Sammy, that's hardly the same, is it?

Nobody answers

Well, it isn't. I mean, all I take is the odd pencil or paper ... clip ...

A slight pause

Well, it's not the same thing at all, is it?

Jack (*to Tina*) Do you steal things?

Tina No. Of course I don't. No. (*After a pause*) Not really. (*Looking at Samantha*) Not like I used to.

Jack Oh, you used to?

Tina No—just the odd ... thing. Jar of jam. Tin of sardines. Nothing. They never missed it. Only when Roy and I were starting out. When we were hard up.

Jack You were never hard up.

Tina We have been, you don't know ...

Jack Yes, I do know. Because I made very sure you never were ...

Tina You may have thought you did——

Jack As soon as you told us you were expecting Kevin, I paid for your wedding, I set you up in a flat and I got Ken to give Roy a job. And I gave you a cash sum as well. Not that we could afford it——

Poppy True.

Jack So don't try that one.

Tina It still wasn't enough.

Jack So you were reduced to stealing things, is that it? You were so poor ...

Tina Yes, we were. (*After a slight pause*) Also I resented paying for them.

Jack Ah, well. Now that's something quite different, isn't it?

Poppy Come on now ...

Tina I resented the vast profits all these firms were making off basic necessities of life we couldn't do without even if we wanted to ...

Jack Bloody hell, let's all sing "The Red Flag", shall we?

Tina Look, don't you make fun—Roy, stand up for me, will you?

Roy Everybody steals a bit, don't they?

Jack Look, what's the matter with you lot? You're just sitting there thinking up reasons for taking things that don't belong to you. That's all you're doing. Am I the only person here who actually thinks it's wrong? It can't be just me, can it? Am I the only one left with any moral values at all?

Poppy Come on, Jack. We're changing the subject.

Jack Well, that's one down, isn't it? Nine to go. Next! Thou shalt not kill. What about that then? Let's have a crack at that one next, shall we?

Tina Dad.

Jack Anybody here object to killing people? No. Right. Good. Carried.

Poppy Jack, for God's sake, don't get so excited. You just fly off at things. You'll have a heart attack or something. He did this with that man just now. Shouted at him and threatened him. If he'd just kept a bit calmer he might have been more co-operative ...

Jack Calmer? Do you know what that man was trying to do? I'll tell you. He was attempting to blackmail me.

Tina Blackmail?

Jack Yes. Employ me and I won't prosecute. Can you believe that? I mean, if I reported that to the authorities he'd be the one in gaol, not Sammy.

Poppy Wait a minute. He said he'd let Sammy off if you gave him a job?

Jack Unbelievable, isn't it?

Poppy So what did you say?

Jack You heard what I said.

Silence

What's wrong?

Poppy You'd rather Sammy went to court than give him what he wanted ...

Jack No, that's twisting it ...

Tina No, it isn't.

Jack Do you realize if I'd given in to him——

Poppy Sammy wouldn't be prosecuted.

Jack You can't give in to a man like that.

Poppy Why not?

Jack Because. Where does it end, for one thing? Anyway, I don't want him working for me. I don't even want him in the same town.

Tina So, Sammy has to go to court ...

Jack You cannot simply buy your way out of things by giving into blackmail and threats——

Tina Dad, we're talking about Sammy's future——

Jack Look, to hell with Sammy, there's a principle at stake here. (*After a slight pause, trying to retract*) No, I didn't mean that.

Samantha turns and runs upstairs again. This time she goes into one of the far rooms, presumably her own. The door slams

Tina (*going after Samantha*) Oh, terrific. That's amazing, that is, absolutely amazing. My own father. Why don't you put the handcuffs on her while you're about it?

Tina goes upstairs after Samantha. She stands at the end of the landing and talks to her sister softly through the door, as before. After a minute or two, Samantha lets her in

Jack Now come on, come on. No need for everyone to start getting over-excited. I've said I didn't mean that, I'm sorry.

Poppy is staring at him incredulously. Roy has dived deeper into his book

I don't know what we're all getting so excited about, I'm sure.

Poppy picks up a couple of glasses and starts for the kitchen

Poppy (*as she goes*) I never would have believed it of you.
Jack (*following her*) What?
Poppy That you'd do that. To your own daughter.
Jack Do what?
Poppy You had a chance to save her and you refused it.

Poppy enters the kitchen and puts the glasses on the draining board. She makes for the sitting-room again

Jack (*following her as he speaks*) Rubbish. All I did was stand up to blackmail and insist she face the consequences of her own actions. She knew what she was doing——
Poppy (*entering the near sitting-room*) Oh, well, let them cut off her hands then, why not?
Jack (*still following her*) It's a good job they don't, isn't it? Or else there'd be very few left in this house with any limbs at all.
Roy Short-handed, eh? (*He laughs*)
Jack (*savagely*) You, shut up!

Poppy takes up a tray of dirty glasses and returns to the kitchen

Poppy (*more calmly*) In spite of what you might think, Jack, none of us are hardened criminals——
Jack (*trailing after her*) I never said you were . . .
Poppy But let me tell you that there have been times when I could have become one without the slightest difficulty. And I have been tempted. God, I have been tempted at times . . .
Jack Rubbish.

Poppy puts the tray of glasses down on the table, transfers them to the sink and, during the course of the next, washes them up. Jack, by reflex, in turn dries them and puts them back on the tray

Poppy (*handing him a tea-towel*) Jack, you are the nicest, most honest, upright, undevious man I have ever met. And I love you for that. I always have done. I've admired you. And I've tried to live up to you, I promise. But I am here to tell you that at times it has not been easy.
Jack What, living with me?

Poppy No, trying to make ends meet ...
Jack We're comfortable enough ...
Poppy Only because I budget down to the last penny, we are ...
Jack We manage perfectly well ...
Poppy Jack, you don't shop. When was the last time you went shopping? I
mean serious shopping. Not just for hi-fi ...
Jack You make it sound as if we're on the bread line. We're both earning,
aren't we?
Poppy Do you think I like going to work?
Jack I assumed you did ...
Poppy Well, you've assumed a hell of a lot, it seems to me ...
Jack Why else are you working?
Poppy Because otherwise we couldn't manage. Oh, we'd live. We'd still live
a bloody sight better than most people, but we wouldn't live in the style to
which you and the kids have gradually grown accustomed.
Jack (*calculating*) Listen, there's my salary plus your salary, which amounts
to what, per annum ... ?
Poppy Gross, an awful lot. Net, not much. I can assure you.
Jack Ah, well. That's the same the world over, isn't——
Poppy No, it is not the same. That's what I'm trying to tell you. Because
everybody else works little fiddles. That's what the system's designed for.
That's what it allows for. Everybody—everybody but us, that is—
everybody else bends it a little; just a little bit here and a little bit there;
and they don't quite declare that; and they tell a little lie about that. Not
dishonest, Jack, just a little bit fuzzy round the edges sometimes ...

*They have finished washing and drying and Poppy has taken up the tray of
clean glasses and started for the near sitting-room*

Jack (*following as before*) Rubbish. You're making out that everybody ...
Poppy (*entering the near sitting-room*) Everybody does.
Roy True.
Poppy You just shut up!

*During the next, Roy, injured, gathers up his book and retreats to the
dining-room and exits*

Poppy starts a furious tidying of the near sitting-room

How do you think Harriet manages three holidays a year because of her
nerves? And Cliff drives that damn great Porsche? And Anita never wears
the same outfit twice? God, I'd kill for some of her clothes ...
Jack Well, don't tell me Desmond's doing better than us. They're not well
off, him and Harriet.
Poppy Only because Des is salting it all away somewhere.
Jack Rubbish. I don't believe that.
Poppy Even him—(*indicating the departed Roy*)—even that—oaf—he's
doing better than we are ... Here I am married to a very successful man,
and we're living like failures. It's not fair.

Poppy bursts into tears, rushes out of the room and upstairs, crying as she goes. Jack follows bewildered

(*From the landing*) Jack, I admire you and I will defend you and your principles with my dying breath, but do you always have to be quite so unbelievably *honest*?

A pause

Jack I see. So, if Sammy breaks the rules and then I bend the rules, two wrongs will make a right? Is that it?
Poppy It has been known.
Jack Well, well . . . Can't trust anyone these days, can you? Even God got it wrong. Poor old soul. (*He heads towards the front door*)
Poppy Jack . . . Jack? Where are you going?

Jack reaches the front door

Jack I'm going down to the *King's Head*. I'm sure, once I'm pissed, I'll see it all much, much more clearly.

Jack goes out and closes the door

Tina comes out of Samantha's room and along the landing to the top of the stairs

Tina Has he gone out?
Poppy Yes. Gone for a drink.
Tina Has he ——?
Poppy Oh yes. He'll come round to it. He'll come round. You know what your dad's like with his principles. (*As she goes along the landing*) Sammy. It's going to be all right, love . . .

Poppy and Tina go into Samantha's room

A lighting change to indicate that the location (if not the setting) has changed. It is late afternoon. The front doorbell rings

In a moment, Yvonne comes from the dining-room. She is apparently in the midst of domestic tasks. She opens the front door to admit Jack. He has on his car coat

Yvonne Hallo, Jack. Ken's expecting you.
Jack Sorry, been a busy afternoon. Trying to get to grips with everything at once.
Yvonne First day at work. What do you expect? (*Indicating her appearance*) Excuse all this, I've been——
Jack You haven't given up looking after him, I see.
Yvonne Force of habit, I suppose. Been nursing him for thirty years at work. Hard to give it up.
Jack You shouldn't need to clean his house for him, though. He can afford someone for that, can't he?
Yvonne Oh yes, she comes in most mornings. That's no problem. I'm just

sorting things out a bit. There's stuff here that hasn't been moved since
Grace died. Her clothes are still in the bedroom; her wheelchair's parked
in the middle of the sitting-room; and there's a jigsaw puzzle on the
dining-room table she was doing the day she was taken ill. They've been
dusting round it for four years ...

Jack Ah, that's sad, isn't it? Gracie never finished it, then?

Yvonne He's upstairs, I think. Want to go up?

Jack (*as he moves to the stairs*) If you ever fancy coming back to work,
Yvonne ... I can always use a good secretary. I don't think much to the
one I've inherited ...

Yvonne Edith's all right.

Jack She's too tall. She frightens me. (*Turning to look upstairs*) How is he
today?

Yvonne Fine.

Jack Comes and goes a bit these days, doesn't he? I mean, last night he
seemed a lot worse.

Yvonne That's because there were too many people. He's never good when
there are too many people.

Jack (*starting upstairs*) I'll see what he wants then.

From the dining-room, a grandfather clock chimes the half-hour

Yvonne Jack.

Jack (*turning*) Yes?

Yvonne Don't—underestimate him entirely, will you? He still knows what's
what better than most of us.

Jack Believe me, I have never underestimated Ken.

Ken comes from one of the far bedrooms and along the landing

Ken Who's that there? Is that Des, is it?

Jack No, it's me, Ken. It's Jack.

Ken Course it is. Course it's Jack. Did she let you in? (*Shouting vaguely in
the direction of the stairs*) Did you let him in, Yvonne?

Yvonne (*calling as she returns to the dining-room*) Yes, Ken.

Ken Good. (*Winking at Jack, confidentially*) She doesn't let people in
unless I tell her to.

Jack Really? (*Looking around*) Well, where do you want us to——?

Ken In here.

Jack What?

Ken Sssh! In here. Not a word.

*Ken opens the bathroom door and, pushing Jack inside, closes and bolts the
door after them. He then reaches in behind the shower curtain, switches on the
shower, flushes the lavatory and turns on the washbasin taps*

Jack What the hell are you doing?

Ken (*above the noise of water*) They have microphones now that can pick up
a pin dropping on Venus ...

Jack (*raising his voice slightly*) On what?

Ken Venus. The big one these days, Jack, is security. No use having the good ideas if they're not secure. Some of those yellow men, they've got them rolling off their production lines before you've had a chance to finish your meeting.

Jack I think it's the other way round these days, Ken.

Ken I know what I'm saying. I fought them, boy. (*Picking up a bathroom stool*) Here. Look at this. See?

Jack One of ours, isn't it?

Ken A Princess Wilhelmina bathroom stool second series, modified. Am I right?

Jack Right.

Ken You're wrong. (*He upturns the stool and shows Jack the trademark on the underside*)

Jack (*reading*) "Donizetti. Made in Italy." Italy?

Ken Right down to the same paint, Jack.

Jack You sure?

Ken I had it analysed. It's a rip off. Even the glue.

Jack What they retailing these at, then?

Ken Roughly twenty per cent above what we are.

Jack *Above?* Then what are we worrying about?

Ken Because the bastards are crowding us out of the market.

Jack How come?

Ken Look at that label, Jack, look at that label. Italian. They'll pay twenty quid more just for that. You know this country. Stick an "i" on the end of your trademark, they'll mortgage their testicles for it. Custom-made designer stools fashioned by Mediterranean craftsmen. All that cobblers. Time was, whatever you bought in this country, you looked for just one word. Birmingham. And you bought it, no questions.

Jack How widespread's this?

Ken Every line we've got, Jack, including the new ones—(*indicating the lavatory*)—flush that again, will you?—I tell you, Jack, they are releasing our new lines almost simultaneous with us. That new three-drawer vanity unit, Miss Felicity, we'd hardly got them out of the drying shop . . . I've tried tracing their end but it's a maze, Jack. It's a ball of string that disappears up some Swiss banker's back passage. We'll have to catch it this end, if we're going to catch it at all. It's an inside job. Someone's selling us short from inside the firm, that's a fact. Industrial espionage. Which is a fancy name for daylight robbery.

Jack Right.

Ken You'll need to take someone aboard. Someone you can trust. Someone sharp who can nose it out. I'll have to leave it to you to choose. Things aren't so easy for me since Gracie went, you know.

Jack I'll deal with it, Ken.

Ken I get the odd blank patch, you know . . .

Jack Yes.

Ken Funny, it just sort of drops away. It's like one minute it's someone you know, the next you can't ever remember meeting them before . . . You see them looking at you and you know they're thinking who the bloody hell does he think I am? And you yourself haven't a notion . . . Mind you, they say it's when you start looking in the mirror and you're puzzled, that's the time you need to worry. Seventy-five next week, you know.

Jack We hadn't forgotten, Ken.

Ken I can leave this with you then, can I?

Jack I'll get moving on it.

Ken Not a word though. That we're arranging to get someone in. Just you and me.

Jack Only us, is that it?

Ken Only us.

Jack Not Yvonne?

Ken (*rather vaguely*) Well, yes, I might have told her. Well, she's my right arm, like. Wonderful girl. Rock solid. Bloody sight more use than her sister, anyway. I wish Des had married her and not the other one.

Jack I hear him and Harriet have got problems, yes.

Ken I warned him when he married her. I said, whatever you do, son, keep clear of thin women. They're trouble. They're for magazine covers only. No use for nothing else. And look at her now. Death warmed up. Don't mention this to Des, either.

Jack No?

Ken I know he's your partner but he's no head for the business. Never has had, more's the pity. My own son. Should have been a cook in a girl's school, that's more his line. The truth is, he's more than half-way to nancy, if you ask me.

Jack Oh, I don't know, Ken ...

Ken You know my Gracie, she was thirteen and a half stone when she died and we never had a cross word. God, she could laugh. Remember her laugh?

Jack Nobody could forget her, Ken (*After a slight pause*) Well, I'll get going then.

Ken Yes, you get off. Want to make use of the facilities, before you go? (*He turns off the taps and shower*)

Jack No, thanks all the same.

Ken opens the door to let Jack out

Ken You'll manage to find someone, will you? For this job?

Jack Yes—I ... I think I've got someone who'll do.

Ken Make sure he's a good man. We need a good man.

Jack Sure. Cheerio.

Ken Cheerio, son.

Jack goes downstairs quite thoughtfully. As he does so, from the dining-room, the grandfather clock strikes six. Ken remains in the bathroom. He is about to leave when he catches sight of himself in the bathroom mirror. He stops and stares, looking slightly puzzled as he examines his own reflection. Jack stands in the hall, looking for Yvonne

Jack (*calling quite softly*) Yvonne?

Yvonne comes hurriedly and a little guiltily out of the dining-room. She has on an attractive (and expensive) brooch which she wasn't wearing earlier

Yvonne Oh, hallo. Are you off?
Jack Yes.
Yvonne Had your talk?
Jack Yes. I gather you know about it——
Yvonne Oh yes. It was me who advised him to get someone in.
Jack Well. We are.
Yvonne Good. I hope you find out something.
Jack I expect we will. See you soon. (*As he goes, noticing her brooch*) That's nice. Your brooch.
Yvonne Oh, yes. It's ... not mine. It was Grace's. I was just seeing how it looked. On me.
Jack Lovely.
Yvonne Yes, isn't it? 'Bye.
Jack 'Bye.

Jack goes out of the front door. Yvonne closes it and goes back slowly to the dining-room, fingering the brooch. Ken has now left the bathroom and has gone off again into one of the far bedrooms

The location changes again. It is evening now, a couple of days later. A rumble of thunder and rain

Poppy dashes in through the back door with an armful of washing. She closes the door and regains her breath. She is wearing a rather smart, up-to-the-minute outfit, slightly but not radically different from her usual clothes

Samantha, meanwhile, is coming downstairs. She is wearing a dress and appears, somewhat reluctantly, to have made an effort

Poppy (*to herself*) I knew I'd forget these ... I knew I would ...

Samantha comes into the kitchen

There you are. You didn't remind me and I forgot them. See?
Samantha I don't know why you still hang the washing out. Why don't you get a drier? Everybody else has a drier.
Poppy (*starting to fold the clothes*) I'm not wasting money on driers when there's good fresh air ...
Samantha Good fresh rain ...
Poppy (*surveying Samantha*) Oh, that's better. You look really nice now.
Samantha I feel stupid.
Poppy Lovely.
Samantha I hate dresses. They're all draughty.
Poppy Well, once you've said thank you to your dad, then you can change into what you like.
Samantha Getting dressed up just for that.
Poppy Thank your lucky stars you're not in prison. You'd have to wear a dress in prison.
Samantha No, I wouldn't.
Poppy You would if they told you to. If they told you to put a dress on you'd soon jump to it. (*Examining her own attire for a moment*) This doesn't look too young for me, does it?

Samantha (*ignoring her*) I'm not seeing that man if he comes, anyway. I'm not talking to him.

Poppy We'll see. (*She has finished sorting the washing. She hands a pile of Jack's underwear to Samantha*) Here. Take these up and put them in the airing cupboard.

Samantha (*recoiling in revulsion*) Yurrr! Yurrr!

Poppy Sammy, don't be so silly, for heaven's sake!

Samantha Yurrr!

Poppy It's perfectly clean. (*Handing it to her*) Now go on and don't be so stupid.

Samantha reluctantly accepts the load

Samantha Yurrk.

As she is about to go, Jack comes in the back door hurriedly running from the rain

Poppy Here he is.

Jack (*shutting the door*) Hey, what a downpour, eh?

Poppy (*kissing him*) Hallo, dear. (*Helping him off with his coat*) You must be tired.

Jack Just a bit.

Poppy You're not going to have to work every Saturday, are you?

Jack I sincerely hope not.

Poppy (*taking his coat to the hall*) I'll hang this up for you.

Jack (*noticing her outfit*) Is that new, is it?

Poppy (*feigning surprise*) Oh, yes. I got it this afternoon. Anita came round and we both went shopping. She helped me choose it.

Jack Oh.

Poppy You don't think it's too young for me, do you?

Jack No, it's fine.

Poppy (*convinced now it's wrong*) Yes. It was Anita, she kept on and on ... (*Giving up*) Anyway. (*Indicating Samantha*) Look who's here to say hallo to you.

Poppy goes into the hall. She hangs up the coat in a cupboard and then goes into the far sitting-room, anxious not to intrude

Jack Hallo, Sammy. All right, are you?

Samantha I'm all right.

Jack Right.

Pause

Samantha (*rather as if she's been rehearsed in this*) Thank you for what you did in getting me out of trouble and I promise I won't do it again and I am very sorry for bringing shame on the family.

Jack (*a little taken aback*) Yes. Good. I'm sorry if I've—er ... I'm sorry. I don't know if I have done anything but if I have, then I'm sorry.

Samantha You haven't.

Jack Good. Fine. Right. Well. Go and sit down, shall we? Till this bloke arrives? Not that I intend to make him very welcome. I would like it known he is here under sufferance.

He moves off into the hall. Samantha follows Jack across the hall to the sitting-room. As she does so, the front doorbell rings. Poppy immediately comes back into the hall

Poppy That'll be Mr Hough. Just stay down a second, Sammy, and say hallo.
Samantha I am sodding not ... (*She rushes upstairs*)
Poppy (*half-heartedly*) Sammy ... She keeps saying that word lately.
Jack For once, I'm inclined to agree with her.

Samantha goes into her bedroom and closes the door

Doorbell

Poppy Now, Jack ... (*She opens the front door*)

Benedict stands there. A clap of thunder

Benedict Good-evening, Mrs McCracken.
Poppy Good-evening, Mr Hough. Do come in. Let me take your ... (*She helps him with his mac*)
Benedict Thank you. Good-evening, Mr McCracken. Not the nicest of weather.
Poppy No, terrible. Do come through.
Benedict Thank you.

Poppy leads him through to the sitting-room. Jack hangs up his coat and follows

What a beautiful house this is.
Poppy Thank you. Do sit down.
Benedict Thank you.

They sit. Jack joins them. He remains hostile to Benedict

May I say how delighted I am that things have worked out.
Poppy Yes, it's good they have, isn't it?

A slight pause

Benedict (*with a look at Poppy*) Do you want me to ... ?
Jack You carry on, Mr Hough. I keep no secrets from my wife. She's an equal part of the team.
Benedict And a very decorative one, too, if I may say so. (*He favours Poppy with a leer*) Well. As soon as I received your telephone call last Thursday confirming my appointment to investigate this matter, I set certain inquiries in motion
Poppy That's quick work. I'd no idea you'd already started.
Benedict Oh, I haven't. Not officially. I don't officially start till next Monday. That was the earliest I could without it looking——
Jack Pre-arranged.

Poppy I see.

Benedict I'm itching to go through those files, though. That's where we'll find him, Mr McCracken. Our man's in there somewhere. He's had access to all the information at the right time, in the right department. He'll have left his thumb print somewhere.

Jack I hope you're right.

Benedict However, what I have been able to do, in the meantimes, is a little inquiring regarding the other end of the chain . . .

Jack Donizetti?

Benedict Precisely. It seemed to me, you see, that if we failed to catch our fly in your ointment at this end, we might be able to trace him back at the other. It's a longer shot, but . . .

Jack And?

Benedict I'm getting warmer. Donizetti is a subsidiary of a company registered in Holland, W.K.P. Limited. W.K.P. is, in turn, owned by Lorelei International who are Spanish based but probably part Libyan, part Brazilian owned. Lorelei, in turn, are little more than an offshoot of a company based somewhere near Milan and trading under the name of Rivetti. That's as far as I've got, so far.

Jack (*thoughtfully*) Rivetti?

Poppy We could sue them, couldn't we? If we're sure it's them?

Benedict Well, you could try.

Jack (*trying to remember*) Rivetti . . .

Benedict But from my experience of international law, that could take the rest of your life.

Poppy Oh? Have you had experience of international law?

Benedict Only indirectly.

Poppy Oh.

Jack (*realizing*) Rivetti!

Poppy Jack?

Jack What?

Poppy Anything wrong?

Jack What? No. Nothing at all. Well, thank you so much then, Mr Hough.

He grabs the bewildered Benedict by the arm and starts to propel him towards the front door. Poppy follows, mystified

Benedict (*startled*) Oh, right . . .

Poppy Jack, what are you——?

Jack Good-night, Mr Hough—Poppy, get his coat—you've been a great help. Thank you so much. I look forward to renewing our acquaintance on Monday.

Benedict Yes, I don't . . . I don't . . . I don't . . . I don't quite see——

Poppy (*handing Jack the coat*) Here you are.

Jack Ta. Sorry to rush you away, Mr Hough. I'm expecting a phone call any minute. (*He thrusts Benedict and his coat through the front door*)

Benedict Yes, right-ho. Goodbye . . .

Poppy 'Bye . . .

Benedict exits . . . Jack slams the front door and now gets his own coat out of the cupboard

Jack, what on earth are you——?
Jack I've got to be wrong. Please God I'm wrong. Tell me I'm wrong . . .
Poppy Where are you going now?

Jack is half-way across the hall and entering the kitchen

Jack I'll be back as soon as I can . . .
Poppy Won't you tell me where you're going?
Jack To see one of Mr Rivetti's business associates . . .

Jack goes out of the back door, leaving it open

Poppy follows him to close it, puzzled

Poppy Mr Rivetti . . . ? Mr . . . ? (*Realizing*) Oh, my God, Mr Rivetti!

Poppy changes her mind and hurries out after Jack, closing the back door behind her

Jack. Wait a minute. You'd better be sure.

Poppy exits

As the door closes, the Lights change to indicate another location. The hall and landing lights are on but the rest of the house is in darkness. The doorbell rings insistently

After a moment, the far bedroom door opens and a figure appears on the landing jumping, trying to get into a rather tight pair of designer jeans. It is Giorgio Rivetti, the strikingly similar younger brother of Uberto whom we met earlier. Giorgio is 25, a freshfaced, attractive, rich young Italian. Like his brother, Uberto, he speaks little English. The doorbell rings again. Giorgio mutters agitatedly to himself. Another figure appears on the landing, naked except for a sheet wrapped round her. It is Anita. In her free hand she holds Giorgio's discarded shirt. He snatches it from her

Giorgio Mio Dio, dovevamo andare in albergo.
Anita It's all right, Giorgio. It's not my husband——
Giorgio Te l'avevo detto che era meglio andare in albergo. Adesso tuo marito è tornato e mi spara.
Anita —it can't be. You're quite safe. Cliff has got his own key. (*With difficulty*) Non è mio marito.

The doorbell rings again. Giorgio yelps in panic

Look, for God's sake, Giorgio, wait there while I get rid of them . . . *Aspetta qui!*

Anita starts downstairs. Giorgio hovers on the landing, nervously

Giorgio Aspetta qui, già . . . Avremmo dovuto andare al Savoy.

The doorbell rings again

Anita Wait! (*She reaches the front door*)

Giorgio goes back into the far bedroom and re-emerges on to the landing with his shoes and socks which he endeavours to put on while listening to what's happening below

(*Talking through the front door*) Who is that, please?
Jack (*off*) It's Jack, Anita ...
Anita Oh hallo, Jack, how are you?
Jack (*off*) Let me in, please.
Anita Jack it's not very convenient at the moment. I wonder if you could come back——
Jack (*off*) Anita, open this door or I'll kick it in.
Anita (*doing so*) Look, Cliff's not here at the moment, Jack, he——

Jack bursts in, pushing her aside

Careful!
Jack Where is he? Where is that brother of mine?
Anita I've said, he's not here.
Jack (*moving first to the kitchen and switching on the lights*) Cliff! (*Seeing the room is empty, he switches off the lights, then crosses to the sitting-room and switches on the light*) Cliff!
Anita How many more times, he's not here. He's down the pub. I promise you, he is. He's got some darts match.
Jack Then call him and get him back here.
Anita I can't do that. It's a match.
Jack Unless you prefer me to go down there and bounce him round the Snug on his head ...
Anita What's he done?
Jack Get him.

Anita picks up the phone and dials

Anita I'll dial him on his mobile, he always has it with him.
Jack Well, he would do. He's a busy lad, isn't he?
Anita I don't know what he's supposed to have done ...

The phone connects

Hallo, Cliff? It's me. ... Listen, can you come back? ... No, now. ... No, I'm sorry but it's urgent. ... No, I can't explain on the phone, it——
Jack (*snatching the phone from her*) Cliff, this is Jack. Now get back here, sunshine. (*He hangs up*)
Anita (*slightly intrigued*) I've never seen you like this before ... You're quite masterful, Jack. (*She giggles*)
Jack You haven't seen the half of it yet. Wait till little brother arrives. I'll——

Giorgio, on the landing, having managed to put on his socks and one shoe, now drops the second with a clatter. He stands, appalled

What was that?

Anita What?

Jack He's here, isn't he? He's upstairs. (*Charging for the stairs*) He's not in the pub at all, he's upstairs ...

Anita No, that's not him ...

Jack thunders up the stairs. Giorgio, hearing this, dives for the near bedroom, looks round, panic-stricken, and decides, with a certain unoriginality, to hide in the fitted wardrobe. He slides open the door and is all but engulfed in Anita's numerous frocks that spring from their confined, undersized quarters

Giorgio Ah! (*He fights his way in with difficulty*)

Jack (*reaching the landing*) Cliff! I know you're here!

Anita (*following him upstairs*) Jack, he's not up there, I swear he isn't. Jack!

Giorgio (*during this*) Oh, Madonna santissima, fa che non mi spari. Te ne prego, non lasciare che mi ammazzi.

Unable to close the door, Giorgio crouches behind the dresses, muttering a prayer. Jack enters the bedroom and stops short as he hears this

Jack Who's that in there? That's not Cliff.

Anita I told you it wasn't.

Jack Who is it, then?

Anita It's Giorgio.

Jack That Italian? The one I met the other night?

Anita No, that was Uberto. This is his younger brother, Giorgio.

Jack How many of them are there?

Anita Five.

Jack Five?

Anita Uberto, Vincenzo, Orlando, Lotario and Giorgio.

Jack All called Rivetti?

Anita Yes.

Jack And you're working your way through them all, are you?

Anita Mind your own business ...

Jack This is very much my business, Anita. I have one or two urgent matters of my own to discuss with the Rivettis ... (*Advancing on the cupboard*) Oy, you! Out!

A terrified scream from Giorgio

Anita Don't frighten him, Jack, he's only a kid. He hasn't done any harm. He's a good boy, he's very religious ...

Jack Yes, I can see he is. Says his prayers regularly in married women's wardrobes. Anita, does Cliff know this is going on?

Anita May I get dressed, please, Jack?

Jack Poor bastard. He doesn't, does he? He's down there playing his darts match and he hasn't got a clue, has he?

Anita Please let me get dressed, Jack.

Jack What's this doing to Cliff? What's it done to him already? Ask yourself, Anita. What is this doing to yourself as a human being? Your husband's due back any minute, you've got a fourteen-year-old Catholic

Boy Scout in your cupboard and you don't give a stuff, do you? You defy belief.

Anita (*wearily*) Oh, God. Hold on a minute, Jack, I'll go and put on some organ music.

Jack I'm not a prude. If people want to bore themselves rigid with soft-porn movies or read newspapers full of tits, I don't mind. I don't want to interfere with that. But surely somewhere, Anita, there's got to be a minimum level of decent human behaviour, hasn't there? Beneath which none of us sink? Like not screwing around in your own marriage bed with men who are busy swindling your own family out of thousands of pounds? Something around that level, eh?

Anita (*calmly*) Oh, I see. That's what all this is about. Sorry, Jack, I was being a bit slow. My mind was still on other things.

Cliff comes in the front door and closes it

Cliff (*calling*) Hallo?

Anita (*calling*) We're up here.

Cliff (*starting up the stairs*) This had better be important. It was a vital match tonight . . . semi-finals. If we beat the Young Farmers this evening, we meet the CID in the final . . . Oh hallo, Jack.

Jack Evening.

Cliff What's the problem? (*To Anita, without undue surprise*) What are you doing?

Anita Jack's just been telling me that someone's swindling the family out of thousands of pounds, Cliff. Do you know anything about that?

Cliff No such luck. Hasn't come my way. What are we talking about then, Jack?

Jack We're talking about furniture, Clifford. We're talking about Ayres and Graces having their designs ripped off and reproduced elsewhere. We're talking about them being resold under a fancy foreign label. Most important of all, we're talking about my own brother organizing the whole bloody racket.

Cliff Who me?

Jack Are you denying it?

Cliff Jack, you know I wouldn't do that. I'd never rip old Ken off like that. You know me . . .

Jack You are lying to me, Clifford. I've known you since you were one day old, boy. Never lie to me.

Jack advances. Cliff retreats

Cliff Now, hold on . . .

Anita Jack, don't hit him . . .

Jack (*loudly*) I want the truth, son, the truth.

Jack thumps the cupboard to make his point. A cry of fear from Giorgio inside. They stop

Cliff Who's that then? Is that Giorgio?

Anita Yes.

Jack (*surprised*) You know about him?
Cliff What's he doing in there? Trying on dresses?
Anita He's hiding from you. He's frightened you'll kill him.
Cliff Me?
Anita It's all right. He's seen too many foreign films.
Cliff Stupid pillock. We'd better all go downstairs before he suffocates. Jack, I'm sure we can sort this out. Let's go down. I've got a nice single malt down there. (*To Anita*) You going to join us, or what?
Anita I'll be down in a second. Wait till I'm there.

Cliff leads Jack downstairs to the sitting-room

Anita goes back along to the spare bedroom

Cliff (*as they go*) When I explain it, Jack, you'll see. It's not as bad as you think, I promise.
Jack (*his mind still on the other matter*) You mean to tell me you knew about Anita? And that boy?
Cliff Yes, I knew.
Jack And it doesn't worry you?
Cliff It's a free country, Jack. She does what she likes, I do what I like.
Jack You're happy the way things are, then?
Cliff You know me, Jack. I've never expected much from life. Why should I expect to be happy, for God's sake?

Anita emerges from the far bedroom in a dressing-gown. She comes downstairs, under the next

Jack Don't you still love her at all?
Cliff Jack, before you leave, have a look out there in the front drive. You'll see a black Porsche 944S Coupé, brand new registration, personalized number plates. That I love. Just through there, I have over three thousand quid's worth of sound gear and a couple of hundred compact discs. That I adore. Just outside Chichester I have a small sailing boat that I would willingly lay down my life for. I am even in love with my new liquid-crystal display digital wrist computer. But Anita? Who needs all that, Jack? I don't. If I want pleasure, I can go for a drive, I can go for a sail, I can blow my head off listening to the Ninth Symphony, or I can even calculate the correct time in Vladivostock if I am that stuck for something to do. Women? Forget them. Quite frankly, I'd sooner play darts.
Jack Well, it's not for me to interfere, but I'd say you definitely have problems, Cliff.

He breaks off as Anita comes into the sitting-room. Her manner now is brisker, less coquettish

Anita What's all this about, then?
Cliff Look, get us all a malt, sweetheart, and I'll try to explain things to Jack.
Anita No. You get the drink. I'll explain.

Cliff hesitates

Go on.

Cliff Fair enough. (*He goes into the far sitting-room*)

Anita What was it you wanted to know?

Jack You don't deny you're doing business with this Rivetti family?

Anita No. We don't deny that.

Jack By helping them to manufacture and sell exact copies of our furniture under their own label?

Anita No. Any furniture we sell, or rather any furniture we resell to the Rivettis and they then resell, that all comes straight from your factory and is delivered to us in your lorries, driven by your drivers.

Jack Just a minute. Are you saying you are reselling our actual furniture . . .

Anita Yes. We're buying it quite legitimately. And then we're reselling it. What's wrong with that?

Jack Selling it under another label?

Anita No.

Jack You know you bloody well are.

Anita When it leaves us, it hasn't got any label on at all.

Jack But it has when it arrives from our factory.

Anita No, it hasn't.

Jack How the hell are you buying goods from our factory without a name on?

Anita I don't know. You'd better ask your factory that, hadn't you? We're doing nothing illegal.

Cliff returns with a bottle of malt whisky on a tray with three glasses

Jack Well, somebody's selling off our furniture via the back door. Presumably at give-away prices?

Anita I don't know.

Jack And who relabels it, then?

Anita I don't know.

Jack Presumably the Rivettis?

Anita I don't know.

Jack (*losing patience*) Now, look——

Cliff (*pleased at how Anita is handling this*) All we know is, Jack——

Anita (*cutting him off*) We don't know anything, Cliff. Nothing.

Silence

Cheers!

Jack (*not drinking*) Well, we'll get one thing straight. This is only the start. I shall follow this right the way through. I shall turn that factory of ours upside down till I find who's responsible for selling us short and, when I've sorted them out, I shall settle the brothers Rivetti, right? There will be no cupboard on this planet big enough to hide them. And if you two happen to be in my line of fire, then all I can say is, God help you.

Cliff (*nervously*) You wouldn't do that to us, Jack.

Anita He would.

Jack And it's not only me you've to deal with. Starting Monday, there will be a voracious little ferret in our midst, diving down rabbit holes, flushing out the black sheep left, right and centre. And I warn you, he's an unstoppable little bastard.

Anita That'll be Mr Hough?

Jack (*startled*) How did you know that?

Anita I go shopping with your wife, Jack. We're friends. I help her choose her clothes. Greater trust hath no woman . . .

Jack (*disconcerted*) Well. That's as may be.

Anita She also told me how you came by him, your Mr Hough. It sounds a bit underhand, Jack. Not like you at all. I mean, I'm sure people would be amazed if they heard . . .

Jack Oh. Oh, now. Don't you try that. Oh. Oh. Oh. Don't think you can try that. Not with me. You won't find me yielding to that sort of blackmail ever, I can tell you. (*Pause*) Hardly ever. If at all. (*Pause*) Very, very, very rarely indeed.

Anita Excuse me. I'm getting rather chilly. Switch off when you've finished, Cliff, won't you?

Cliff Right you are.

Anita goes upstairs and goes into the far bedroom

(*Smiling rather nervously, now he is alone with Jack*) Bit of a stalemate then, eh?

Jack Who is it selling you our stuff, Cliff?

Cliff I don't know.

Jack No, don't you try that. You're not as clever at it as she is. Now who? Who's behind it all? There's got to be one person, somewhere, hasn't there, fairly high up? Who?

Cliff I don't know.

Jack (*moving closer*) Cliff . . .

Cliff (*covering his head and retreating*) It's no use hitting me—I won't tell you.

Jack I'm not going to hit you.

Cliff You are.

Jack I've never hit you. When in the whole of our lives have I ever hit you? Even as kids——

Cliff You used to tickle me . . .

Jack Listen, Cliff. If I promise—if I give you my word as a brother that I'll keep you out of it, will you tell me?

Cliff I daren't.

Jack My solemn promise. Now you know my promise, Cliff. Since we were kids, have I ever broken it?

Cliff Your solemn promise?

Jack Yes.

Cliff All right. (*A nervous glance after Anita*) Des.

Jack Des? You mean Desmond?

Cliff Yes.

Jack (*incredulously*) Are you talking about *Desmond*? Desmond?

Cliff Yes.
Jack My partner, Desmond Ayres? My so-called bloody partner? Desmond-bloody-Ayres? The man's own son? I don't believe it. I just don't believe it. (*He storms out of the sitting-room and towards the front door*)
Cliff Jack? Where are you going?
Jack Heads are going to roll. I can promise you, heads will roll. Desmond Ayres!

Jack goes out of the front door, slamming it behind him

Cliff stands a little bemused in the hall

Anita comes out of the far bedroom. She now has her nightdress on

Anita What's going on?
Cliff I'm afraid I had to tell him. About Des . . .
Anita I thought you might. Where's he gone?
Cliff You know how Jack can . . . I think he's on his way round to Des's . . .
Anita You'd better phone Des. Warn him Jack's coming.
Cliff Right.
Anita And then phone round everyone else. We'll have to have a meeting.
Cliff Tonight?
Anita As soon as we can. I'll get dressed.

Cliff goes to the sitting-room phone and starts to dial. Anita enters the near bedroom and goes to the cupboard to select herself something to wear. Giorgio's startled face appears as she ruffles through the dresses

Anita (*startled*) Oh, hallo, lover, I'd forgotten all about you. (*Selecting a dress*) Later. I'll be back soon. *Presto. Presto.*
Giorgio (*kissing her hand, eagerly*) Presto! Presto!
Anita (*more interested in deciding what to wear with the dress*) Yes . . .

She absent-mindedly closes the cupboard door on him and moves off to the far bedroom

A telephone bell rings as Cliff is connected and the Lights come up on the kitchen

Desmond comes in through the back door. He has been to empty the rubbish-bin. He is in his shirt-sleeves and is wearing his cook's apron. He answers the kitchen phone

Desmond Hallo. Desmond Ayres speaking.
Cliff Des? It's Cliff. I'm just phoning to warn you. He's on his way.
Desmond What? Who's on his way?
Cliff Who the hell do you think?

Before he can speak further, a massive hammering is heard on the front door, together with Jack's angry voice. From the dining-room, the yapping of a small dog

Jack (*from outside the front door*) Desmond! Open this door! Desmond!
Desmond What on earth's that?

Cliff (*fearing he is disconnected*) Hallo ... hallo ...

Harriet's head appears through the hatchway

Harriet (*alarmed*) Desmond, there's someone at the front door. (*To the dog behind her*) Quietly, Peggy, quietly.
Desmond (*petulantly*) Well, you'll have to let them in, Harriet. Let them in. I'm on the telephone.
Harriet I don't know who it is. Oh. (*She disappears back through the hatch*) Peggy, stop that.

Jack continues to hammer on the door, shouting occasionally. The dog continues to yap. Desmond returns to the phone

Desmond Hallo. Sorry, Cliff, someone was at the door. What were you saying?

Harriet comes out of the dining-room, gently pushing the dog back with her foot and closing the door. She prepares to open the front door

Cliff It's Jack. He knows everything. He knows about you.
Desmond Jack does?
Cliff It's probably him at your door ...
Desmond Oh, my God. (*Dropping the phone*) Harriet! Don't open the——

Harriet has opened the hall door

Jack stands there like an avenging angel

Jack (*with a terrible roar*) Desmond!

Harriet cringes, Desmond steels himself, Cliff listens alarmed and the dog yaps on as——

BLACK-OUT

ACT II

The same. It is afternoon

Upstairs Poppy is round at Anita's. The dresses we saw crammed in the wardrobe are now strewn around the near bedroom. Poppy is trying one on. Anita, who is dressed as if ready to go somewhere, is perched on the bed watching

Downstairs, Harriet sits in the near sitting-room resting on the sofa. Nearby, an enclosed dog basket with presumably an unseen animal inside. In his kitchen, Desmond is busy preparing supper. As he does so, he listens to a Teach Yourself Spanish cassette on his portable player. Occasionally, he attempts to join in rather unconvincingly. He checks the casserole in the oven and, fetching a cookery book from a shelf, settles at the table and studies it during the next, switching off the tape

Poppy What do you think?
Anita Yes. It's all right. It's only pulling very, very slightly round the hips.
Poppy Yes, they all do a bit. I keep meaning to lose some.
Anita It would let out. I know it would. I had it taken in for me.
Poppy It's lovely.
Anita Take it if you want it.
Poppy Sure?
Anita I'm sick of it.
Poppy It's hardly been worn.
Anita Oh, I'm like that, I'm afraid. Three days and I can't stand the sight of most of my clothes.
Poppy I hate all mine, too, but I still keep wearing them.
Anita Depends what you choose to spend your money on, I suppose. With me, it's clothes. And shoes. (*Reflecting*) And jewellery. You choose to spend it on something else. Presumably.
Poppy (*rather sadly*) I don't spend mine on anything.
Anita Mind you, I don't pay full price for anything. It's all back door.
Poppy (*surveying herself again*) Yes, I like this very much. I don't know if I've any shoes, though.

Anita opens a bedside drawer and produces a box of expensive jewellery— evidently her cast-offs. During the next, she tries various items on Poppy

Anita Pity we're not the same size. I could have given you those.
Poppy He must be doing very well.
Anita Who?
Poppy Cliff.

Anita He does all right.

Poppy I mean, for you to be able to afford all this.

Anita This? This is nothing to do with Cliff.

Poppy Isn't it?

Anita (*trying a necklace on Poppy*) No. I bought all this.

Poppy Oh, I see. I'm sorry, I——

Anita I'm a hard-working girl, me.

Poppy I see.

Anita Who do you think runs our business then? Cliff? (*She holds a brooch to Poppy's breast*)

Poppy I am sorry. You know, I never realized . . . well, I knew you worked but I never realized . . . I thought you must have—well, I don't know what I thought really—I thought you just had a job like mine. You know. Ordinary. Sorry.

Anita (*reproachfully, as she tries ear-rings on Poppy*) You'll have the heavy women after you, you know . . .

Poppy Yes, I know. Awful. I'm sorry. It's just, you know, you see Cliff driving around in his smart car and you naturally think——

Anita The reason he drives round in that, dear, is because I bought it for him for Christmas. Only don't let on I told you or he'll die of shame.

Poppy Well.

Anita Mind you, I mustn't lie, I do accept the occasional little gift— occasionally. (*Displaying the gold bracelet she is wearing*) Now, I didn't buy this. Pretty, isn't it?

Poppy Lovely. Where did it come from?

Anita (*putting away the rest of the jewellery*) I don't know. Italy, I suppose.

Poppy (*slightly embarrassed*) Oh, yes. Of course.

Anita Well, if you ever feel like a bit of relaxation. A nice evening out—just let me know. I could probably fix you up.

Poppy What?

Anita With someone nice.

Poppy What, a stranger?

Anita He needn't be strange for long.

Poppy You mean for—money . . . ?

Anita No, no, no. Amateur status, love. Must keep that, mustn't we? Otherwise you are on the slippery slope. No, you can accept heartfelt tokens of appreciation, that's all. But they've got to be heartfelt. (*Glancing at her watch*) Where's Cliff got to? We must go soon. Anything else you want while you're here? (*Selecting another frock*) What about this one. This'd suit you . . .

Poppy Well, if you're going out . . .

Anita You've got time to try this on. Look, come into my bedroom. I've got the full-length mirrors in there. You can see yourself properly.

Poppy Are you sure?

Anita (*gathering up the dresses*) I'll bring them all through, just in case . . .

Poppy This is very generous of you—I feel so guilty.

Anita (*moving to the landing*) Along here. You haven't seen my bedroom, have you?

Poppy (*following her and taking her own rather dull original dress with her*) No, I don't think I have.
Anita Now, this I'm rather proud of—What do you think?

Anita leads Poppy to one of the far bedrooms and goes in

Poppy reaches the doorway and stops momentarily

Poppy (*in total amazement*) Oh, my goodness! Oh, good Lord. What are they all for?

Anita laughs. Poppy cautiously enters the bedroom

Harriet comes swiftly into the hall from the near sitting-room and opens the front door. Desmond, unaware that this is happening, continues his reading

Jack is standing outside, on the point of knocking

Harriet (*slightly frostily*) Hallo, come in, Jack.
Jack Oh, thank you, Harriet. Saved me from using the knocker.

She closes the front door. Jack waits to be directed somewhere

Harriet If you could be as quiet as you can, Jack. Peggy's asleep in the front room . . .
Jack Peggy?
Harriet Ssssh!
Jack Oh, the dog. Yes, of course.
Harriet That's why I was looking out for you. To prevent you from using the knocker. Otherwise she'd have been disturbed again.
Jack (*solicitously*) Yes, I see.
Harriet She was up all last night, you know. Three thirty a.m. before she settled. Before each of us could settle, come to that.
Jack You and Des?
Harriet Me and Peggy. Desmond slept all right. Out like a light as usual. Take more than that to give him a sleepless night.
Jack Yes. (*Awkwardly*) Harriet, I presume I was the cause of the trouble. I just want to apologize for yesterday. Bursting in here like that. I can only say—I'm sorry.
Harriet Well.
Jack Truly sorry. The point is that, overnight, I've thought about things in a more—calm—light and——
Harriet (*coolly*) I think you had better say that to Desmond rather than to me, Jack.
Jack Certainly, yes. Where is he then? In the kitchen, I presume. (*He laughs*)
Harriet (*unamused*) Would you step in here for a moment first, please? (*She indicates the near sitting-room*)
Jack (*rather startled*) Yes, by all means.

He and Harriet go into the near sitting-room

Harriet (*once they are safely inside*) I wanted to say this out of Desmond's earshot . . . Whatever it is that's going on—and you will appreciate that I realize something is going on with Des and his business—whatever it is, I am no part of it whatsoever.

Jack No, I didn't for a minute think——

Harriet I have no knowledge of it, I have had no benefit from it. Anything at all that Desmond has accrued as a result of his—dealings—I have seen not one penny of.

Jack That's entirely understood.

Harriet I am blameless. I am not to be implicated. Any criminal proceedings that may arise from all this cannot involve me . . .

Jack Harriet, listen. There is no question of criminal proceedings.

Harriet (*a trace of disappointment*) There aren't?

Jack Well, I hope not.

Harriet But surely——

Jack What I'm hoping is that we can sort this out as a family matter. Agree, between us, to put our own house in order. We shouldn't need to resort to the law.

Harriet But surely, what has been going on is criminal . . .

Jack I thought you said you had no knowledge of what was going on?

Harriet I don't. But I'm not a fool. I've had my suspicions. You can't live with the man without having those.

Jack (*a slight pause*) You didn't, by any chance, mention your suspicions to your sister?

Harriet Whatever do you mean?

Jack Did you mention this to Yvonne?

Harriet I can't remember offhand. I may have done.

Jack Even though you knew she was bound to tell Ken?

Harriet Well, he had a right to know, anyway. He had to be told something was going on.

Jack Well, he was told. And sooner or later, he's bound to find out that Des is involved.

Harriet Perhaps he will.

Jack I don't know what it is Des has done to you, Harriet, but you've certainly got it in for him, haven't you?

Harriet (*defensively*) That's completely untrue. I'm not the one who shuts myself away—who refuses to talk, refuses to communicate at all unless it's about—onion soup.

Jack I'm sure that's not true, Harriet.

Harriet You live with him. You try living with him. You know something? Do you want to know how I feel about food and eating recently?

Jack No?

Harriet I saw a film about this once by that man who's dead. And I agree with him. Eating is an obscene act. That's what I think. Restaurants and cafés with people sitting in front of each other in public, shovelling food into their mouths, it's actually pornographic, isn't it? Don't you agree?

Jack Er—no, I don't think I do really . . .

Harriet I do. I think it's disgusting. Looking at all their fillings and—

bridgework and tonsils ... I'd sooner watch people do—you know—the other thing, than that.

Jack What other thing?

Harriet In the ... you know ... in the little girls' room.

Jack Would you really? Well. There's no accounting for taste, Harriet. I think, on the whole, I'd still prefer a meal ...

Harriet It's the chewing, I think, all that masticating in front of each other ...

Jack Yes, OK, Harriet. I really must get a word with Des now.

Harriet Look. Look. Ssh. Ssh. Before you go. (*She beckons him*)

Jack (*warily*) What now?

Harriet indicates the dog basket

Harriet Look. Look at her. Sound asleep. Have you ever seen anything so daft?

Jack Oh, yes. Incredible to be able to sleep like that, isn't it?

Harriet (*gazing with real love*) Yes.

Poppy and Anita come out of the bedroom. Poppy has changed back into her own clothes and carries a couple of dresses she has chosen. Anita has her coat on

Poppy I've never seen such a collection of—things. I must be terribly innocent, I don't even know what half of them are for ...

Anita Oh, darling, don't ask. Over the years I've accumulated so much gear. You'd need a degree in engineering just to lie down in that bedroom.

Poppy It's more like a stable. Does Cliff go for all that, then?

Anita I wouldn't know, love, I've never asked him. Don't forget your handbag.

Poppy Oh, heavens.

Poppy goes into the near bedroom. Anita steps into the bathroom and checks her appearance in the mirror

(*Alone to herself*) Well, I don't know, I'm sure.

Jack Yes. It's an unusual-looking dog, that. Quite old, is he?

Harriet She's thirteen.

Jack Unusual. Those pink areas, are those the natural markings?

Harriet No, her fur's rubbing off there. It's where she scratches herself. Can you hear her? Snoring?

Jack Oh, yes.

They stand listening. Anita and Poppy have now reached the hall

As they do so, Cliff opens the front door with his key

Cliff Come on then. Come on.

Anita We're going to run Poppy home first, OK?

Poppy It's very kind of you ...

Anita Then I said we'd pick up Orlando ...

Cliff (*noticing Poppy's armful*) What have you got there?

Anita I've been introducing Poppy to the spoils of the good life . . .
Cliff Naughty, naughty.
Anita And not before time, poor woman.

They go out of the front door closing it behind them

Jack Well. I'd really love to listen to her snoring all day, Harriet, but . . .
Harriet Yes, of course. He's in the kitchen. Can you find your way? I'm
    afraid I can't go anywhere near the place myself, I hope you'll under-
    stand. If I were to go in there, I'd——
Jack Yes, yes, yes, yes. Quite all right.

*Jack hurries across to the kitchen and opens the door gently. Harriet, after a
moment, gathers up the dog basket and retreats to the far sitting-room*

Des?
Desmond (*looking up from his book*) Oh. Hallo, Jack.
Jack (*sniffing the air*) Smells interesting.
Desmond Yes. I think this might turn out quite interesting. Lancashire Hot
    Pot.
Jack Ah. Yes, lovely . . . yum-yum.
Desmond I didn't hear you arrive.
Jack Harriet let me in. She was anxious I didn't disturb her dog.
Desmond Oh yes? Well, she had a bad night.
Jack Yes.
Desmond So did I, actually.
Jack I think we all did.
Desmond Well . . .
Jack I wanted to say, I'm sorry about—last night—I——
Desmond No. That's all right. Quite. I mean, no.
Jack I mean, I said a lot of things . . .
Desmond No, no, no. I mean. No. It's me who's—yes.

Pause

(*Rather nervously*) What are you planning to do then?
Jack I'm planning to sort things out, Des. Get things back on the straight
    and narrow.
Desmond Yes. (*Seeing Jack isn't going to reveal much more*) I've arranged
    for the others to be here. They shouldn't be long.
Jack Then I'll save it all till then.
Desmond Yes.

Pause

Jack I feel you ought to know that it was Harriet who told Yvonne about
    all this. Who subsequently tipped off Ken. Who subsequently told me.
Desmond Yes. That's logical. I think she went through my things while I
    was at work. My papers. My own fault, I shouldn't have left them lying
    about. She obviously felt I was salting it all away somewhere.
Jack But weren't you?

Desmond Oh yes, I was. She was quite right. But I wouldn't have seen her short. I'd have left her well provided.

Jack Left her?

Desmond When I went.

Jack (*startled*) Went where?

Desmond goes to a kitchen drawer and after rummaging under a layer of tea-towels, etc., produces a creased colour prospectus for a new holiday village

Desmond I keep everything in here, she never comes in here . . . (*Showing the leaflet to Jack*) Look. See.

Jack Where's this? Greece?

Desmond No. The Balearics. Minorca.

Jack Oh.

Desmond See that? That's partially finished. It's going to be part of the new complex. You see, it's got the golf course, shops, swimming pool, social club. These are the villas. And that there—(*pointing*)—that's my restaurant.

Jack What are you saying? You're going to work in a restaurant?

Desmond No, I've bought it. I've bought the lease. I own the franchise.

Jack You're going to run it?

Desmond Chef owner. It's been a dream, Jack. For years.

Jack You put all that money into this?

Desmond And the villa. That's mine, see? (*Pointing to the map*) Number seventy-eight C.

Jack Looks a bit small.

Desmond Well, I don't need much. There's only me.

Jack You're going to live there on your own?

Desmond Yes.

Jack Serving Lancashire Hot Pot to a load of ex-patriate, golf-playing old age pensioners? You'll be up the bloody wall in ten minutes, Des.

Desmond I'm half-way there now, Jack. Look, if you try and stop me from doing this, it would kill me, it really would. The thought of this is the only thing that's holding me together these days.

Jack What about Harriet? I mean, she's—she doesn't seem so good, now. What's she going to be like if you suddenly take off with your chef's hat in your suitcase? I mean, when did she last eat, for God's sake? She's like a praying mantis . . .

Desmond (*suddenly quite savagely, for him*) Oh, she eats, don't worry about her. She just likes people to think she doesn't. But I've caught her. Kendal Mint Cake.

Jack Really?

Desmond Packets of it. She hides them in the dining-room behind the dog food, but I've seen her through that hatch.

Jack She can't survive on just Kendal Mint Cake, can she? All her hair'll start falling out or something.

Desmond That wouldn't bother me. She'd match that dog of hers then, wouldn't she? (*Agitatedly*) Look, she can eat in here any time she wants.

It's up to her. I've said to her, any time you want. I've even offered her a choice of menu.

Jack You mean to tell me, that you've been bleeding dry your own business, the business your father spent fifty years of his life putting together, a business dozens of people have given the best part of their lives to—just to open a bloody restaurant ...

Desmond (*angrily*) It's my business.

Jack It's not your business, it's his business. No, it's not even that, it's ours. All of ours. It's our business.

Desmond (*shouting like a child*) Well, it ought to be mine. That's all. It ought to be mine, so there. (*He starts to cry*) What does a man have to do ...

Jack Oh, Des. Don't do that, please. It's hard enough without——

The door knocker sounds

Desmond (*sobbing*) I've given up a lot of my life as well. Bloody chairs and tables and sink units and bidets ...

Harriet hurries from the sitting-room to open the front door

Jack That someone at the door, is it?

Desmond Yes, I'll ...

He grabs a handful of kitchen towel and makes his way to the hall, blowing his nose as he goes. Harriet, meanwhile, has opened the door to ...

Roy standing there

Roy (*cheerfully, to Harriet*) How do you do?

Harriet (*frostily*) Hallo. (*To Desmond*) I wonder if you could ask your friends to come to the back door, please. Peggy is trying to rest and so am I.

Desmond All right, dear, all right, I will ...

Roy You want me to go round the back door?

Harriet Ssshhh!

Roy Sorry.

Harriet How many more times? Peggy is asleep.

Desmond (*whispering*) Go through, Roy.

Roy (*stepping inside*) Wilco. Thank you.

Desmond I'll wait out here and redirect the others when they arrive.

Desmond goes out of the front door

Harriet (*to Roy*) Shut the door, then. Or Peggy'll be out on the main road.

Roy Sorry. (*He closes the door*) Walks in her sleep, does she?

Harriet (*icily*) You know the way.

Harriet goes into the dining-room. Roy enters the kitchen. Jack, who has been reading the leaflet, looks up in surprise

Roy (*rather sheepishly*) Hallo, Jack.

Jack Oh, no. Not you as well?

Roy Yes.

Jack It's just about everyone, isn't it? All we need now is the Pope.

Roy Didn't you know? That I was involved?

Jack No. Des just said he was going to get everyone round here.

Roy Everyone?

Jack Well, all the—important ones.

Roy I was going to say. Not everyone. You'd need to book the football ground.

Jack (*sharply*) This is not a joke, son.

Roy (*hastily*) No, no. I know it isn't.

Jack It is no laughing matter at all. So wipe that bloody silly smile off your face . . .

Roy Right.

Pause

Jack Where's Desmond?

Roy He's re-directing the others.

Jack (*irritably*) What?

Roy To the back door.

Jack Oh.

Pause

Roy If you—if you didn't know I was involved—I needn't have come round, need I?

Jack Too late now, isn't it? You should have worked that out before you came.

Roy I didn't know before I came. I only knew when I came. Too late then. I'd have to have known before I came. Then I wouldn't have come if I'd known.

Jack (*studying him for a second*) You've got all the reasoning powers of a draught excluder, haven't you? How much does Tina know?

Roy Nothing.

Jack Is that the truth?

Roy Promise. She doesn't know a thing about it. I was frightened she wouldn't approve.

Jack (*rather bitterly*) Oh, I don't know.

Roy There's a horrible smell in here. What's he cooking?

Jack Lancashire Hot Pot, I think.

Roy So long as he's not expecting us to stay and eat it, that's all. He's a horrible cook.

Jack Is he?

Roy He's motorway material, I tell you. Haven't you been round here to eat since he got this chef kick?

Jack No, I don't think we have. Poppy doesn't get on too well with Harriet . . .

Roy (*looking at the cookery book*) Lancashire Hot Pot. That could start the Wars of the Roses all over again, couldn't it?

A rapping on the back door and a rattling on the handle. It is Desmond accompanied by Anita, Cliff and Orlando, 30, the middle-most of the five Rivetti brothers. He is the family man, plumper and jollier than the two relatives we met previously, but with no better command of English

Hang on. (*He unlocks the door*)

All troop into the kitchen. Desmond follows them up and closes the door

Anita Hallo, Jack.
Cliff Jack.
Jack Hallo.
Roy Afternoon, all.
Anita This is Orlando, Jack. Orlando Rivetti. *Questo è* Jack.
Orlando Salve.
Jack *Ciao.* How do you do?

An awkward silence

Desmond Well, shall we all sit down?

They all do so. All are understandably wary of Jack

Excuse us having to meet in here, everyone. Only Harriet's having to be with Peggy in the living-room and besides, I need to keep an eye on the stove.
Roy A thieves' kitchen, eh?

He laughs. Nobody else does. A slight pause

Desmond Perhaps you'd all like to stay for a bite to eat after our meeting?

Nobody responds to this offer

You'd be very welcome. Obviously, we'll have to see how the meeting goes first. (*Looking nervously towards his brother-in-law*) Jack? Do you want to kick things off?
Jack If this is everyone who's meant to be here ... I gather it is—I don't want to say much. Most of you must have guessed how I feel about this. I think probably disgust is the word that springs to mind. Disgust that a group of people whom I regarded not only as friends but also as relatives—most of you—should conspire to swindle an old man, a sick old man out of his life's work.
Desmond We were always going to see him right, Jack.
Jack (*ignoring him*) That is all I have to say on that matter. All right? We are going to clean this up, all right? We are going to sponge the shit off the family name, all right? That's what we're here to do today. We are going to put the business back together as it was. As a decent, honest, small family business. So. How do we go about that?
Roy Difficult.
Jack I'll tell you. We start with that end. (*Indicating Orlando*) We stop doing business with them to start with. *Arrivederci* Donizetti, all right?
Anita (*to Orlando*) *Dice che dobbiamo smettere di fare affari con voi ...*

Orlando Si. Arrivederci Donizetti. (*He laughs*)

Jack Oh, we've got the laughing one today, have we?

Anita He doesn't speak much English . . .

Jack Never mind, they seem to muddle through, don't they? (*To Cliff and Anita*) Secondly, there will be no more cut-price sales to your lot, all right?

Cliff If you say so, Jack.

Jack I do. Thirdly—(*he turns to Desmond*)—we put our production line back to producing bona fide company products, all right? Sold through the proper outlets at the correct prices. All right?

Desmond Yes. (*Looking at Roy*) All right, Roy?

Roy Well, the lads aren't going to like it . . .

Jack (*outraged*) The lads aren't going to like what?

Roy Well, you know, losing the extra. I mean they'd sort of come to rely on it.

Jack Then they're going to have to rely on working for their money instead, aren't they?

Roy But they're bound to take a drop, Jack . . . I mean, their basic wage is only——

Jack If their basic isn't enough they'll have to clock overtime, won't they?

Roy They'd have to do another seventy hours a week to make up what they'd be losing . . .

Jack Too bloody bad!

Roy All I'm saying, Jack, is they're not going to like it . . . you could have trouble.

Jack (*excitedly*) I don't believe this. Are you threatening me with industrial action because the workforce object to being told they can no longer swindle the firm they're working for? It defies belief. It——

The hatch slams open and Harriet sticks her head through

Harriet Would you mind keeping your voice down in here, please? There are other people in this house.

A startled silence

Thank you.

Harriet closes the hatch sharply, comes out of the dining-room and returns to the far sitting-room

Desmond Best to keep our voices down a bit. It's safer if Harriet doesn't hear what we're——

Anita She knows far too much already . . .

Desmond Ah, now, we don't know that necessarily——

Anita Of course we do. Who else told Yvonne?

Jack (*anxious to proceed*) So.

Desmond Sorry, Jack.

Jack So. That is what's going to happen. All right?

Anita Could I just——?

Jack No. No discussion. No choice in the matter. That is it. Close of meeting.

Anita Please. (*Faintly sarcastic*) Mr Chairperson, sir?

Jack (*suspiciously*) What?

Anita Just before we go, I just wanted to ask what you intend we do about our friend Mr Hough? In considerably less than a week, he seems to have found out quite a lot about us. He's either got supremely good powers of detection or he's had the good sense to talk to Yvonne . . .

Desmond Now we don't know that necessarily——

Jack (*over-riding this*) He doesn't know much. He knows about the Rivettis, that's all.

Anita He knows Des and I are supplying them. Because he phoned me this morning. He wants to meet me tomorrow sometime.

Jack And he starts with our firm tomorrow morning.

Desmond Oh, my God . . . that's it then, isn't it? That's it. (*He rises agitatedly*)

Jack All right, all right, Des . . .

Desmond That's it! It's all over!

Anita (*sharply*) Desmond! Sit down and shut up!

Desmond sits again. They reflect

Jack All right then, I'll cancel him. I'll phone him tonight and tell him we no longer require his services. That solves it.

Cliff You'll need to pay him off.

Jack I will. I'll tell him to submit his account for the work done to date.

Roy He'll need more than that.

Jack What are you talking about?

Anita (*as to a child*) What they're saying, Jack, is Mr Hough might not be totally satisfied with his standard payment. Considering the amount of information about us he has already gathered . . .

Jack Are you suggesting he'll try to blackmail us? (*A slight pause*) Again?

Anita I'm suggesting he'll probably need paying . . .

Jack watches the next in stunned amazement. The ensuing business discussion happens with great rapidity

Desmond How much are we talking about, then?

Anita Ten maximum.

Cliff How many of us are there . . . one, two . . . don't count Jack . . . three, four, five . . . Five? Can we go to ten?

Desmond Ten? I can't go to ten . . .

Cliff No, two . . .

Desmond Still a lot.

Anita We could start with five. Hold back five.

Cliff In reserve.

Roy Two maximum.

Desmond Five up front.

Anita Five behind. Right?

Roy Done.

Cliff Carried.

Desmond OK.

Jack What's going on? What's going on?
Anita (*to Orlando*) *Duemila lire sterline. Ciascuno. Diecimila. Come assicurazione. D'accordo?*
Orlando (*laughing at this*) Con un premio simile mio fratello ti combinerebbe un'assicurazione molto più permanente.
Jack What's he saying, now?
Anita Orlando says for that sort of premium his brother could arrange something more permanent . . .

Cliff laughs

Jack Like what?
Orlando (*laughing*) Un'assicurazione contro gli incidenti, eh?
Anita (*laughing*) He says, accident insurance . . .
Cliff What? Like accidentally falling out of a fifth-floor window . . . ?
Roy Accidentally swallowing his magnifying glass?

Orlando makes a cheerful choking gesture with his hands, for Jack's benefit

Jack If this is intended in any way as a serious suggestion——?
Anita No, no, Jack. Orlando's joking, isn't he? (*Kissing Orlando on the top of his head*) Oh, I love this one best of all. Do you know he's got six children? *Sei bambini, si?*
Orlando (*reaching for his wallet*) Sei bambini, si . . .
Jack Look, just a minute. Just a minute . . .

Under this, Orlando is passing round photos of his family to any who are interested

Orlando (*during the next*) Questa è la più piccola, Maria. Ha due anni. Quella è sua madre. E' una bella donna, vero? Questo è mio figlio maggiore, Rodolfo. Ha otto anni e già vuol fare l'architetto. Queste sono le gemelle, Lucia e Lucrezia, il giorno del loro quarto compleanno . . .
Jack . . . what is going on here?
Roy We're just sorting out how much we need to give him, Jack.
Jack Give who?
Roy This Mr Hough.
Jack We're not giving him anything. Except what he's earned . . .
Desmond But, Jack——
Jack No. I've had enough of this. No more of it. You understand.

Orlando tries to interest Jack in a family snapshot

No, I don't want to see. Put them away. *Avanti!* (*To others*) Let me make this quite clear. I have no intention of indulging in any more blackmail, bribery, corruption or anything else. Is that understood? From now onwards, all our business is going to be conducted above board. My God, if we start giving five hundred quid here and five hundred quid there to every——
Roy Thousand.
Jack What?
Roy I think we're talking about thousands, Jack. Ten thousand.

Jack (*stunned*) Ten thousand quid. You're joking.

Desmond It might be only five.

Jack You are joking ... I am boggled ...

Cliff It's about the going rate, Jack ...

Jack I am just—boggled ... I mean ...

Desmond (*hopefully*) You don't think Jack could get him for five hundred, do you?

Anita Never.

Cliff Jack ought to do it, though.

Jack What?

Anita Yes, you'll have to be the one to deal with it, Jack.

Jack You want me to do the bribing as well?

Anita Seriously. It'll have to be you.

Jack (*rising in fury*) That's it. No more. Not another word ...

Cliff Wait a second, Jack. Wait a sec ...

Anita It has to be you, Jack. You're employing the man.

Jack Good day. I am leaving now before I commit damage.

Desmond (*vainly*) Jack! Don't go that way, please ...

Jack Goodbye.

Despite their protests, Jack stamps out through the hall and out of the front door, which he shuts with a thunderous slam

From the sitting-room, the dog starts yapping. They look alarmed

Harriet (*shouting angrily from the sitting-room*) Who did that?

Desmond Quickly. Out the back. (*He goes swiftly to the back door, opens it and starts shooing his remaining guests out*)

Anita, Cliff and Orlando exit

As they do, a furious Harriet comes out into the hall

Harriet Someone did that deliberately ... deliberately ... (*She goes back into the far sitting-room*)

Desmond Quickly ...

Roy Don't forget your Hot Pot ...

He exits

Desmond (*turning, appalled*) Oh, my God. My Hot Pot!

Harriet returns to the hall clasping the dog basket. She opens the front door. There is no-one there. Desmond searches about for his oven gloves

Harriet Deliberately ... you did that deliberately!

Harriet goes out of the front door closing it behind her

Desmond works to salvage his meal. He opens the oven and withdraws a blackened, smoking, open casserole dish of what was once Lancashire Hot Pot

Harriet, meanwhile, has come round the house to the back door, still clasping the dog basket

(Off, as she approaches) Desmond! I will never forgive you for this, Desmond ...

She appears in the back doorway

Desmond *(turning to her, the casserole still in hands)* Harriet, I'm sorry I ...

Harriet sees what he is holding and recoils in horror, covering her mouth with her hand to stifle a scream. Then, overcome with nausea, she rushes back into the garden with a final, terrible moan

Desmond follows her out, clasping his ruined casserole to him like a child

Harriet ... ?

It is now evening and we are back at Jack's and Poppy's

Tina, dressed to go out for the evening, comes from the dining-room. She carries a children's picture/story book. She starts up the stairs. As she does so ...

Poppy comes out of the spare bedroom (i.e. not Samantha's). She is wearing, just a trifle self-consciously perhaps, one of the dresses Anita has given her. A child's voice is heard from the spare bedroom

Poppy All right, Mummy's coming. Stay in bed.

Samantha comes into the kitchen through the open back door. She is wearing her school clothes and a motor-cycle helmet. She carries a piece of electrical equipment—we can't tell what it is—wrapped up in an old sheet. A plug dangles from a mains lead, which is the only indication as to what it might be. Samantha places her load on the kitchen table, having checked the coast is clear. She now hurries out again, leaving the door open

Tina and Poppy meet on the landing

Oh, he's been calling for you ...

Tina It's all right, I'll read him this. It's so boring it always sends us both off to sleep. He hasn't woken Michelle, has he?

Poppy No, she's well away. I'm sorry they've got to be in the same room tonight but I couldn't face Sammy again ...

Tina It's all right. It's not a problem. *(Regarding Poppy)* That's really nice, you know, that suits you.

Poppy *(doubtfully)* You sure? I think it probably looked better on Anita ...

Tina Why? Why should it? You've got as good a figure as she has.

Poppy Oh, I haven't really. *(Studying herself)* I think I'm a bit too old for it really.

Tina Rubbish. You look amazing. Really.

Poppy Really?

Tina Really.

Poppy *(still doubtful)* Well. *(Then, giving up worrying)* You and Roy going to the cinema, did you say?

Samantha, helmetless, comes back into the kitchen under the next

Tina Yes. We haven't been for years. Be nice. We're going to see—what's it called—you know. With what's-'is-name. With the—with the thing. You know.
Poppy That'll be nice.
Tina Yes.

Samantha shuts the back door. The sound of a two-stroke motor-cycle starting up and receding is heard

Poppy Well, I——(*She stops as she hears this. Calling*) Sammy? Is that you?

Samantha freezes in the kitchen. They listen

I thought that was her.
Tina Late, isn't she?
Poppy You know what that school's like. All these societies and clubs and things. She often stays on late. She's got a friend who gives her a lift home.
Tina Eastwood. Clint Eastwood.
Poppy That's the one. I must go down. Jack'll be back soon. He's got this man coming. (*She starts downstairs*)
Tina (*stopping her*) Roy told me, you know, about all that at work.
Poppy Oh, did he? I didn't know if he'd——
Tina Yes. Last night. (*Smiling*) I don't know, I'm sure . . .
Poppy (*half amused, despite herself*) Terrible, isn't it? I mean, all that going on. And your Uncle Desmond as well.
Tina And Uncle Cliff.
Poppy What a family, eh?
Tina And Auntie 'Nita.
Poppy Yes, well. Her. I don't think anything would surprise me any more as far as she's concerned . . .

A child calls from the spare bedroom

Tina (*calling to the bedroom*) All right, I'm coming, love. (*To Poppy*) You know it's awful really but—ever since Roy told me about all this business and him being involved—I sort of respect him more for it. Not less. Isn't it awful?
Poppy Well . . . it is, really.
Tina I mean, I'd—I'd got really sick of him, I can't tell you. I mean, that's dreadful, isn't it? The man I loved—had my children with—promised to share my life with—and my heart used to sink when I heard him at the door. I mean, some evenings I used to sit and pray he'd been run over, just so's we wouldn't have to talk to each other . . . There. Isn't that awful? I feel so ashamed even saying it. But now all this business. Well, he can't be completely daft, can he? Otherwise he couldn't . . . Well, if you're going to be a criminal you've got to have some sort of brain, haven't you? I mean, any fool can be honest, can't they? You know what I mean?
Poppy (*doubtfully*) Yes, I think so. I don't know your dad would agree, though.
Tina (*laughing*) Well, he wouldn't, would he? That makes him out a complete idiot, doesn't it?

Poppy (*laughing with her*) True.

A child calls again from the spare bedroom

Tina All right, Kevin, here I come.

She moves off along the landing. Poppy starts downstairs and goes into the sitting-room to turn on a couple of lights. Samantha listens till she is sure her mother is in there

(*As she goes into the bedroom*) What do you want, darling?

Tina goes into the bedroom

Samantha picks up her bundle from the kitchen table and starts upstairs. Poppy comes out of the sitting-room with the ice-bucket on her way to the kitchen

Poppy Sammy?
Samantha (*nonchalantly*) Oh hallo, Mum.
Poppy You're late, aren't you?
Samantha I had a meeting.
Poppy Oh, that's nice. Which one was it tonight?
Samantha The Musical Appreciation Society.
Poppy Lovely. What have you got there?
Samantha Gramophone records. My friend lent them to me.
Poppy Well, don't play them too loud, will you?
Samantha No.
Poppy Use the headphones Uncle Cliff gave you.

Samantha continues up the stairs. Poppy goes into the kitchen and fills the ice-bucket

Tina, at the same moment, comes out of the bedroom with an empty water glass

Tina (*calling behind her*) Well, you're not having much more of this or you'll wet the bed . . . Oh hallo, Sammy.
Samantha (*scowling*) Oh, no. You haven't dumped your foul, horrible, disgusting baby in my room again, have you?
Tina No, I have not. And don't be so rude. She is very beautiful. What have you got there?
Samantha Nothing.
Tina What? What have you stolen now?
Samantha Don't tell Mum. (*She unwraps the bundle partially to reveal its contents*)
Tina Whatever is it?
Samantha CD player. Compact disc.
Tina Sammy! Honestly, you're mad. Haven't you got enough sound gear already? It's like Abbey Road Studios, your room.
Samantha I'm not having this, I'm reselling it.
Tina Why?
Samantha Because I need the money, that's why.

Tina What for?
Samantha To buy things.
Tina What things?
Samantha Things. Mind your own business. (*After a pause*) Things.
Tina Oh, Sammy, you're not into that, are you?
Samantha Into what?
Tina You know what I'm talking about. Those things—whatever you call them. Drugs. Are you into drugs?
Samantha Sssh! No.
Tina Truthfully.
Samantha No! Not seriously, anyway.
Tina Sammy, they're terribly dangerous. They keep telling you . . . they can kill you, you know.
Samantha So can picking your nose with a screwdriver . . .
Tina Oh, don't be so childish . . .
Samantha Look, you don't know anything about it. It's only if you do it regularly. I'm not doing it regularly. I can't afford to, anyway.
Tina Sammy . . .
Samantha Bugger off, Tina. Go and pot your baby . . .

Samantha goes into her bedroom and shuts the door

Tina looks worried. She goes into the bathroom, fills the water glass and then returns to the other bedroom. As she does this . . .

Jack enters through the back door. He is wearing his coat and carries an attaché case which he clutches rather tightly, while holding it slightly away from him as though it were red hot. Cliff follows a little way behind. He has on his driving gloves but no coat. He carries a heavy-looking adjustable spanner

Poppy (*going to kiss him*) Hallo, love. Just in time for a drink.
Jack Oh, good. I—er—brought Cliff back.

Cliff appears round the door

Cliff Hallo.
Poppy Oh hallo, Cliff.
Cliff Hallo.

An awkward pause

Poppy How was your day, then?
Jack What?
Poppy Your day. How was it?
Jack Oh, my day? My day was fine, yes.

Pause

Cliff Nice dress.
Poppy Thank you. (*After a slight pause*) It's your wife's.
Cliff Really? I don't think I've seen it before. I must have been glancing at my watch while she was wearing it. (*He laughs*)

Poppy Are you going to take your coat off, Jack?
Jack Oh, yes.
Poppy (*helping him*) Here. Cliff? Can I—take your ... (*She eyes his spanner*) No ... you want to keep all that, do you?
Cliff Yes, thanks.
Poppy Well, shall we move through to somewhere more comfortable, shall we?
Jack (*starting to move into the hall*) Right.

Cliff does not move

Poppy Cliff?
Jack No, Cliff'll stay there.
Cliff I'll stay here.
Poppy What, in the kitchen?
Cliff Fine.
Poppy (*baffled*) Yes. Suit yourself. Would you like a drink?
Jack No.
Cliff No.
Poppy No. I can leave the light on, can I? ·
Jack No.
Cliff No.
Jack But leave the door.
Cliff Please ...
Poppy Yes ... (*She turns off the kitchen light*)

Poppy is mystified. Jack stands awkwardly in the hall, still clutching his attaché case for dear life. Cliff paces round the kitchen a couple of times and finally sits

   Jack, what's going on? Why's Cliff ... ?
Jack Sssh. Come in here a second. (*He indicates the sitting-room*)
Poppy Just a minute.

Poppy goes to hang up Jack's coat. Jack puts the briefcase down on the table and stares at it

   (*From the hall*) Did you say you wanted a drink?
Jack Yes, I did. Thanks.
Poppy I'll get you one.

Jack produces a key and swiftly unlocks the attaché case. A few bundles of ten pound notes spill on to the floor. He stuffs them back in the case and stares at the contents in horror. Then, shaking his head in disbelief, he closes the case again as he hears Poppy returning with the drinks. She stares at him

   You all right?
Jack Cheers.
Poppy Cheers.

They drink

Jack I've got this—man—turning up in a minute.

Poppy Mr Hough? Yes, you told me.
Jack Did I?
Poppy On the phone.
Jack Oh, yes.
Poppy At lunchtime. (*After a slight pause*) What's that?
Jack What's what?
Poppy (*indicating*) That. What's that?
Jack That? That's a—that's a briefcase.
Poppy Is it yours?
Jack No.
Poppy Oh. What's in it, then?
Jack Nothing. Just paper. Bits of—bits of paper. (*He stares at the attaché case unhappily*)
Poppy Jack, you're lying, I know you are. Tell me. We never lie to each other. What have you got there? Tell me.
Jack It's—only money. Just money. That's all.
Poppy Money? How much money?
Jack (*hoarsely*) Masses. Masses and masses and masses of money. Quite frankly, I have never seen quite so much money in one small space. It makes your eyes water, I can tell you.
Poppy (*awed*) Jack, what have you done?
Jack Nothing.
Poppy You didn't steal it, did you?
Jack (*indignantly*) Of course I didn't steal it.
Poppy I'm sorry. Of course you didn't. I don't know what I'm saying . . .
Jack It's just to—it's just to pay Mr Hough, that's all. When he comes. I'm going to have to pay him.
Poppy Jack, what's happening? Suitcases full of money and people hiding in the kitchen with spanners . . . ?
Jack That's just protection, love. Cliff's my protection, that's all.
Poppy You never used to need protection . . .
Jack No, well, this is a special circumstance. I'm walking around with a lot of . . . It's a one-off, I promise. I pay him the money. Clear the family name. Then that's it. No more. Back to normal. I'm having no more of this, I can tell you. I'm really not, Poppy.
Poppy I wish I believed that.
Jack It's true. This is the last bloody favour I'm doing that lot, I can promise you.

A slight pause

Poppy It's my fault. I got you into this.
Jack That's rubbish.
Poppy You should never have listened to me. They say this is what happens. Right through history. With all great men. Brought down by a woman. I'm just like what's-'er-name in the Bible . . .
Jack What are you talking about?
Poppy (*tearfully*) Whatever she's called. You know, the one with the scissors . . . I'm as bad as her . . .

Jack Poppy, I don't have the faintest idea what you're talking about, I'm sorry. Scissors? Look, I'll deal with this bloke and then if you like, why don't we both——?

The doorbell rings

Oh, hell ...
Poppy All right. I'll let him in.

Cliff opens the kitchen door cautiously

Cliff (*calling across the hall*) All right, Jack?
Jack (*urgently*) Stay in there! I'll shout if I need you ...

Poppy goes to the front door. Jack paces about nervously and arranges the case on the coffee table

Poppy admits Benedict

Benedict (*heartily*) Good-evening, Mrs McCracken. My, don't we look attractive tonight?
Poppy Do we? Thank you very much, Mr Hough. (*She relieves him of his coat*)
Benedict I believe your husband is expecting me.
Poppy Yes, indeed he is. (*Leading him towards the sitting-room*) Can I get you a drink of any sort, Mr Hough?
Benedict Well, perhaps a small gin with just a dab of tonic would be very pleasant ... Ah, good-evening, Mr McCracken.
Jack Mr Hough.

Jack invites him to sit. Benedict does so. Poppy goes and pours Benedict his drink

Benedict I trust you've had a good day?
Jack Yes. Thank you. And you?
Benedict Extremely successful, I'm pleased to say, Mr McCracken.
Jack (*disappointed*) Oh. Good.
Benedict I think you're going to react to some of my findings with some consternation, Mr McCracken. Probably even a little shock ...
Jack Really?
Benedict (*slyly*) Unless of course, you've already heard something?
Jack Depends what *you*'ve heard, Mr Hough.
Benedict Precisely. (*He laughs*) We shall see.

Poppy has entered and now hands him his drink

Thank you so much, Mrs McCracken.
Jack Thanks a lot, love. Don't hang around on our account. I know there's things you want to be seeing to ...
Poppy (*who was about to sit down*) What? Oh. So there are. Yes.
Benedict Aren't you staying with us to ... ?
Jack No.
Poppy No. I have—things to be getting on with. In the kitchen. Excuse me.
Benedict Of course.

Poppy leaves, seems a little lost as to where she should go. She contemplates the kitchen but, remembering Cliff is there, she finally opts for the dining-room

Good health.
Jack Cheers.

Benedict drinks. He then puts down his glass and opens his notebook

Benedict Now, then. If I may proceed ... ? The first thing I set out to discover, having successfully located the existence of the Rivetti connection——
Jack Er ... Mr Hough——
Benedict —was whether ... Sorry?
Jack I think, actually, there's little point in going on with your report.
Benedict No?
Jack You see, in fact, I've decided—against proceeding any further. Under the circumstances. I hope you'll understand my reasons.
Benedict Oh yes. Right. That's perfectly understood. (*He puts away his notebook*) Saves a lot of time.
Jack I had no idea when I first asked you, of course.
Benedict No ...
Jack Otherwise I would never ...
Benedict Oh, no ...
Jack So, what I am saying is ... we're trying to keep this in the family as it were ... not involve too many outsiders.
Benedict Such as myself?
Jack Precisely.
Benedict Or the police?
Jack Yes. No.
Benedict None the less, we are talking about a large-scale fraud, are we not?
Jack Oh, it is in hand. Let me assure you things are in hand.
Benedict So, I take it Mr Ayres has been informed about it——
Jack Er. No, no. Under the circumstances, what with ... with certain persons being involved——
Benedict His whole family, for instance ...
Jack Yes ... if you will ... we felt ... it could be very upsetting for an elderly man in frail health, on the verge of celebrating his seventy-fifth birthday——
Benedict Yes. But I do feel Mr Ayres should know, though. Someone should tell him. He ought to know, oughtn't he?
Jack Well, that's a—that's a family decision, Mr Hough. We shall no doubt all be discussing it fully, in due course. All I need to say to you at this stage is, thank you for your help and impressive—assistance and ... perhaps you'd send us your account. In your own good time.

A silence. Benedict stares at him

(*Slightly nervously*) Does that seem fair enough to you?
Benedict Frankly no, Mr McCracken. It doesn't seem fair to me at all.
Jack Ah.

Benedict Not fair to anyone, in fact. Not to the firm, not to Mr Ayres, not to me nor indeed, most important, to the course of justice.

A slight pause

Jack Yes, well. Fair enough. I meant to add, of course, that—that we were all—when we talked—so impressed with your—work to date—Mr Hough—that it was generally felt overall that a—bonus would be in order. A cash bonus. (*After a pause*) A large cash bonus.
Benedict I see.
Jack The figure talked of was five thousand pounds. (*A slight pause*) Five thousand pounds. Cash.

A chilly pause

I don't know how that strikes you.
Benedict It strikes me as most offensive, Mr McCracken.
Jack Ah. (*After a pause*) I—er ... now, where did I put it? (*He slaps his pockets*) ... I may have got it slightly wrong, the sum ... you know, I've had a head full of figures all day ... it could have been nearer six thousand, now I come to think of it ... where did I—? I wrote it down somewhere ...

Jack opens the attaché case so that Benedict gets a clear view of the contents, then closes it again

No. It's not in there. No, I'm almost certain now I think about it, that it was six. Six, seven, something like that.
Benedict (*quietly*) Mr McCracken, what is the maximum sum you have been authorized to offer me?
Jack Ten.
Benedict Ten?
Jack Yes. Thousand. (*With sudden courage*) That's it. Take it or leave it.
Benedict I'm afraid you're left with it, Mr McCracken.
Jack Well, that's that. (*Making to shake hands*) It's certainly refreshing in this world, Mr Hough, to meet an incorruptible man. I'm sorry I——
Benedict Oh, no, Mr McCracken, I'm eminently corruptible, don't worry on that score. It's just that I do have a very good assessment of my own worth.
Jack Yes. I see. And that ... ? Roughly? Would you care to put a value on that, Mr Hough? On your worth?
Benedict Shall we say fifty thousand?
Jack (*blinking*) Yes. Well, I have to tell you, Mr Hough, you can take it from me, right now—that you are whistling up a gum tree, old chum.
Benedict Believe me, Mr McCracken, if this is not resolved to my satisfaction, I shall be whistling on every street corner until you cannot see across this room for blue uniforms. I have some idea of the sums involved over the years—maybe you don't. Just thank your lucky stars I'm not demanding a ten per cent finder's fee or I could be into you to the tune of a quarter of a million pounds. You tell that to your—associates.

Jack (*rather shaken*) Yes. I will. Right. Now, you mean? Right. I shall need to—telephone, you understand. Will you excuse me a moment?
Benedict Of course. (*Glancing at his watch*) I don't have a lot of——
Jack Neither do I. Excuse me. (*He goes to the door, remembers the briefcase, returns and walks out with it, maintaining as much dignity as he can muster*) Excuse me.

Benedict remains calmly seated and relaxed, sipping his drink. Jack goes into the hall, closing the door behind him. Cliff comes out of the kitchen. Poppy comes out of the dining-room

Cliff Well?
Poppy Well?
Jack (*indicating that Benedict is still there*) Shhh!
Cliff Did he take it?
Jack No, he did not.
Poppy He didn't?
Jack (*to Poppy*) Shhh! (*To Cliff*) He wants thousands.
Cliff How much?
Jack Fifty grand.
Cliff Fifty!
Jack I'll have to contact Des. See if he can raise any more.
Cliff What now?
Jack He's waiting for an answer.
Cliff Des won't be able to raise ten grand. He's got it all invested in saucepans . . .
Jack Sssh! Well, he's going to have to find it . . . (*He picks up the hall phone and dials*)
Cliff Who are you phoning?
Jack Des.
Cliff Well, don't say too much . . .
Jack Why not?
Cliff Certain dog lovers listen on the extension.
Jack (*replacing the phone*) What are we going to do, then? This bloke's waiting for an answer.
Cliff Go round and talk to Des.
Jack Now?
Cliff Sssh! Won't take a minute.
Poppy (*indicating Benedict*) What about him in there?
Cliff He can wait. We won't be long. Come on, we'll take my Porsche . . .
Jack I'm not riding in that thing.
Cliff Come on.

The doorbell rings. Benedict reacts briefly, then returns to his drink

Poppy That's probably Roy. (*She goes to open the door*)
Cliff Good, we'll need him . . . see how much he can raise.
Jack What about you and Anita?
Cliff What?
Jack Can you find ten grand apiece?

Cliff I greatly doubt it. I'll have to check with Anita. She handles the joint account.

Poppy lets Roy in the front door

Roy Hallo, then. Is she ready to go?
Poppy Er ... no. There's been a slight ...
Jack (*moving to the sitting-room, still clutching the attaché case*) I'll tell him to hang on here.
Cliff Roy, come on, lad, you're coming with us ...
Roy No, we're going down the Odeon——
Cliff Business, Roy, business ...
Roy Oh, right, wilco.

Tina comes out on to the landing from the children's bedroom

Cliff picks up the phone in the hall. Jack opens the sitting-room door. Benedict turns

Jack Excuse me, one moment, won't you, Mr Hough? I'll be just five minutes. (*He closes the door*)
Benedict Yes, I ... (*He frowns, then returns to his drink*)
Tina (*calling downstairs*) I'm coming ...
Roy Just a sec, love, there's been a change of plan——
Tina (*indignant*) A what?
Jack Sssh! (*He indicates the sitting-room. To Cliff*) What are you doing?
Cliff Warning Des we're coming.

The phone rings in the kitchen

Jack I thought we weren't to use the phone.
Cliff It's all right if you use the code ...
Jack The code?
Tina What is happening, please? Exactly?
Jack Sorry, Tina. We'll bring him back in ten minutes.

Desmond comes breathlessly in through the back door. He is in his shirt-sleeves and apron. As he does so, the hatch opens and Harriet's angry face appears

Harriet Desmond, are you going to answer that or not?
Desmond Yes, love, I was just recataloguing the deep freeze ...
Tina We've missed the start now, anyway. It's hardly worth going. He'll have shot everyone by the time we get there.

Tina goes back to the bedroom rather crossly

Desmond answers the phone

Desmond Hallo. Desmond Ayres speaking.
Roy (*after Tina*) Sorry.
Cliff Hallo. Des mate, it's Clifford. I won't talk for long. We may have another crossed line.
Desmond (*looking round apprehensively*) Yes, yes. Could be.

Cliff Just wanted to check the recipe you gave us a couple of days ago.
Desmond Oh, yes?
Cliff I'm afraid you might not have given me the correct quantity of sugar
  . . . we're coming round. All right? (*He hangs up*)
Desmond (*alarmed*) But you can't have any more sugar——(*Realizing he is
  speaking to no-one*) Oh, my God . . .
Cliff OK, we're on our way, come on.

*Cliff moves to the front door. Roy follows him. Desmond locates a cashbox
which he keeps concealed beneath his oven. He sits during the next and studies
the contents—mostly bonds, bank statements and share certificates*

Jack (*meanwhile, aware he still has the attaché case*) Hang on. What about
  this thing. I'm not carting this all round the houses.
Cliff (*from the front doorway*) Leave it behind.
Jack Poppy, listen, love. Hide this. Put it somewhere safe.
Poppy Why?
Jack Look, there's ten thousand quid in here, right . . .
Poppy Oh, dear God. (*She looks faint*)
Jack Easy, easy . . . (*Changing his mind*) No. Look, it's all right. I'll take it
  with me, it's just as easy.
Poppy No, no. I was just being stupid. I'm a grown woman and I got you
  into this. Now, give it to me at once.
Cliff (*calling*) Come on . . .

Jack, slightly startled, hands her the briefcase

Jack All right, love, fine. Good. (*Indicating Benedict*) But whatever you do,
  don't let him near it, will you?
Poppy No, I won't.
Jack Don't even let him know you've got it. Hide it, then there won't be a
  problem, all right?
Poppy Yes.
Jack Guard it with your life, girl.
Poppy I will.

Jack kisses her

Cliff Come on, Jack. We're only going round the corner.
Jack (*as he goes*) How are we all going to fit in that thing?
Cliff We'll fit, we'll fit. It's a two plus two.

  Roy, Cliff and Jack exit, closing the front door

*Poppy is left holding the attaché case which she handles as though it were filled
with dynamite*

Desmond (*studying his papers*) Oh, my God . . . I can't sell that. I can't
  possibly sell that. How can I make croissants?

*Benedict comes to the living-room door and opens it. Poppy instinctively
flattens herself to the wall to avoid him seeing her*

Benedict (*calling, softly*) Hallo ... Mr McCracken? (*He listens*) Mr
   McCracken?

*Puzzled, Benedict goes back into the room, closing the door. After a moment
he sits down again. Poppy cautiously creeps upstairs. When she reaches the
landing she looks around for somewhere to hide the attaché case. In the end,
she decides to slide it under the bed in the near bedroom. As she walks on the
floor above, Benedict looks up*

   Tina comes along the landing

Tina Mum?
Poppy (*jumping*) Oh! Hallo, dear.
Tina I wondered who it was creeping about. Have they all gone out?
Poppy Yes, all except ... Mr Hough. He's still here.
Tina What, down there on his own?
Poppy Jack won't be long. (*She turns off the bedroom light*)
Tina You sure you're all right?
Poppy Of course. Is Kev asleep yet?
Tina Very nearly.
Poppy I'll say good-night, then ...
Tina You've said it once.

   Poppy goes off to the far bedroom. Tina follows, puzzled

*As they go, there is a knocking on the back door. Desmond jumps, stuffs away
his papers, hastily reconceals the cashbox and opens the door*

   *Jack, Cliff and Roy enter. Roy appears to be suffering from the confinement
   of the journey*

Roy (*as they enter*) Bloody hell, Cliff, couldn't you find a smaller car,
   mate ...
Cliff There's plenty of room ... Hallo, Des.
Desmond Hallo, Cliff. Jack ...

They close the back door. Desmond stares at them apprehensively. A pause

Jack I don't know how I got into all this, I really don't.
Desmond Well?
Jack Our Mr Hough wants more, Desmond. You underestimated. How
   much can you raise?
Desmond How much does he want?
Cliff Fifty.
Desmond Fifty! Oh, no, Jack ... that's impossible ... there's no way I could
   ... fifty? No ...
Cliff Then how much could you?
Desmond Well ... four.
Cliff Four? You miserable——
Desmond Seven if I sell the confectionary oven. But it's a German make,
   they're like gold to get hold of ...
Jack Then you should get a good price for it. Right. That's seven from you.
   Plus two from Roy ...

Roy By selling the rotary mower . . .
Jack Plus ten we've got already. Nineteen. We've got thiry-one grand to find, haven't we, genius?
Desmond (*pointing to Cliff*) What about him? What about those two? They're rolling in it.
Roy You could sell that car . . .
Cliff I'm not selling that.
Jack If needs be we will auction your internal organs round the back of the General Hospital, Clifford.
Cliff Well, we'd better talk to Anita. She knows better than me . . . (*He takes the kitchen wall phone and starts to dial*)
Desmond You're not phoning her? Not on the phone?
Cliff Just to warn her we're coming . . .
Jack Come on. Get your pinny off . . .
Desmond Me?
Jack We need everyone.

The phone starts ringing in the near bedroom

Roy There's no room for him in the back of that thing.
Jack You can manage, it's only half a mile.
Roy I'm running behind you.
Jack You're staying with us.

From the far bedroom, Anita comes along the passage. She has on her basque corset and leather thigh boots, one of which she was apparently only half-way into when the phone rang. She is cursing as she limps and hops to the phone

Anita All right, all right. Just a minute, just a minute. I knew these bloody things were a size too small . . . (*Savagely into the phone*) Hallo.
Cliff Hallo . . .
Anita Cliff? Look, what the hell do you mean by ringing up . . . ?
Cliff Hallo, cherub, I'm at Des's so I won't talk for long. It's a very bad line. We need your advice on the recipe . . .
Anita On the what?
Cliff The recipe. R—E—double C——
Anita All right, I know how to spell it, what about it?
Cliff I'm afraid it's going to need gingering up . . .
Anita All right. Come on round then. (*She hangs up*)
Cliff She's in a filthy mood . . .
Anita Oh, balls, balls, balls and bugger. (*Calling*) Vinchy! Vincenzo! We're going to have to stop for business, love, I'm sorry. (*She switches off the bedroom light*)
Vincenzo (*distant, muffled*) Aiuto! Venite! Anita! Aiuto!
Anita Oh, hang on, sorry. I'd better let you out of there, hadn't I? *Vengo* . . . Don't jump about, for God's sake, or you'll strangle yourself.

Anita goes back into the far bedroom

Desmond has taken off his apron and rolled down his sleeves

Cliff Come on, Des.
Roy How are we going to fit him in?
Cliff It's not far.
Desmond Do I need a coat ... ?
Jack If he puts an overcoat on, he's riding on the roof.
Cliff (*leading the way out*) Away we go, then ...
Roy (*as they leave*) See you, Harriet!

They go out, closing the door

The hatch opens and Harriet glares out

Harriet More sugar? Ginger? What's he making now?

She closes the hatch

Benedict, meanwhile, has risen and moves to the door again. He opens it and steps into the hall

Benedict (*calling again softly*) Hallo! Anybody about? (*He seems worried. He moves to the kitchen door, opens it and goes in. During the next he looks round the kitchen and opens the back door and peers into the darkness outside*)

Meanwhile, Anita comes along the landing, fastening her dressing gown. She has both her boots on properly now. She is followed by Vincenzo. He is a thin, stooping, rather nervous figure of 28. Bespectacled, academic and rather shy. He, too, is pulling on a bathrobe but is barefoot, with just his trousers on underneath

Anita (*as they come downstairs*) Siamo nei guai col detective ...
Vincenzo Chi?
Anita L'investigatore privato che ha fatto l'inchiesta. Vuole altri soldi ...
Vincenzo Dovreste dire a mio fratello Lotario di farlo fuori. Vi costa meno che pagare quello lì, a lungo andare ...
Anita I don't know what you're saying, love, but you're probably right. Come on, we'll have a drink. *Qualcosa da bere.*
Vincenzo Si, beviamo qualcosa.

Anita and Vincenzo go into the far sitting-room and get drinks. Benedict comes out of the kitchen and moves towards the dining-room

Benedict Hallo? (*He goes into the dining-room*)

As he does so, Poppy comes out of the far bedroom a little way. She stands listening. Tina follows her on to the landing

Tina What is it?
Poppy Nothing, I thought I ... heard something. I—nothing.
Tina Shouldn't you see if he's all right down there? That man?
Poppy He's all right. He's got a drink. (*After a slight pause*) Actually, I don't really want to be with him on my own, really. He gives me the creeps a bit.

Tina What him? That little man? (*She laughs*) Want me to come down with you, then?

Poppy Yes, all right. Once you've got him to sleep.

Tina I don't think he intends to tonight. Little horror. I wish he slept like Roy.

Tina and Poppy return to the far bedroom. As they do so ...

Cliff opens the front door with his key and lets in all the others. Jack, Roy and Desmond—all of whom are now suffering the after-effects of their constricted journey

Cliff Come in. (*Calling*) 'Nita?

Anita (*coming out of the far sitting-room*) We're in here.

Roy (*gaping at her*) 'Strewth!

Anita What are you gawping at?

Cliff For God's sake, love, couldn't you even find time to put your clothes on? What do you think you're doing?

Anita A little light housework, my angel.

They troop into the far sitting-room. As they do so, Benedict comes out of the dining-room and looks about the empty hall

Benedict (*to himself*) Curiouser and curiouser ... Mrs McCracken? (*He starts climbing the stairs*)

The group in the sitting-room, Jack, Anita, Roy, Cliff, Desmond and Vincenzo came through to the near sitting-room. They seat themselves during the next. Only Anita and Vincenzo have drinks

Anita Well, what's all this in aid of? He wants more money, I take it.

Jack He wants fifty. You're thirty-one light. Can you make it up?

Anita What? Ready cash?

Jack Yes.

Anita Absolutely not.

Desmond Not if you sold something?

Anita If we sold something we might, yes ...

Roy That car of his for starters ...

Anita (*thoughtfully*) No, we can't sell that. I didn't buy it through normal channels ...

Desmond (*agitated*) Well, you've got to find it, somehow——

Cliff (*angrily*) Look, why is it us selling things——

Jack All right!

They pause for a moment. Benedict reaches the top of the stairs. He looks into the darkened bathroom

Benedict Mrs McCracken? (*He switches on the light and looks round the bathroom. After a second, he switches it off again*)

Desmond All my money is already tied up. It's heavily tied up.

Cliff Well, untie it then ...

Jack Listen. Listen, you lot. I'm going to say this once. You either come up

with the money or that's that, all right? I'm leaving you to fend for
yourselves.

Roy Oh, don't be like that . . .

Jack Sort it out between you. Because I don't intend to spend the rest of my
life acting as your bagman and wandering round with trunk loads of
small change.

*Benedict goes into the near bedroom and turns on the light. He is now very
wary*

Benedict Hallo . . . ? (*He studies the room for a moment before turning out the
light*)

Jack You've got five minutes. Because I've left him sitting at home waiting
for an answer.

Roy Well, I haven't got ten.

Jack What about him? Italy?

Anita This is Vincenzo. You met his brothers.

Roy If you get the set, you can trade them in for a gallon of petrol. (*He
laughs*)

Cliff I don't think we can ask the Rivettis again. Apparently their mother
got very upset about the last two grand.

Jack Well, I do look forward to meeting her as well, sometime. Coming
back to my original question, where are you going to find it from?

Benedict (*starting along the landing towards the far bedrooms*) Mrs
McCracken?

Anita Would—you . . . ? I wonder if you'd excuse us a second, Jack, while
we sort this out between us?

Jack That's all you've got. A second.

Anita We'll be as quick as we can . . .

Jack (*making to rise*) Right, I'll . . .

Anita No, sit there. We'll go next door. All right? Come on everyone. Next
door.

*Anita leads them all except Jack back into the dining-room. Jack sits waiting
impatiently, now and again glancing at his watch. Benedict is almost at the far
bedroom door*

Benedict Mrs McCracken . . .

*Poppy comes out of the bedroom and nearly collides with Benedict. She
yelps*

Poppy Oh!

Benedict Mrs McCracken . . .

Poppy Oh, I'm sorry. I do beg your pardon, Mr Hough, I——

Tina comes hurrying out of the bedroom

Tina Mum? Are you all right?

Benedict No, I beg your pardon, Mrs McCracken. I had no intention of
startling you . . .

Poppy No, I'm sure . . .

Benedict I was merely trying to ascertain if there was anyone left in the house besides myself ...

Poppy I'm sorry we—abandoned you rather. I was just seeing to my grandchildren ...

Benedict (*sentimentally*) Ah!

Poppy Have you met my daughter, by the way? This is Tina.

Tina How do you do?

Poppy This is Mr Hough ...

Benedict Yes, she's as lovely as her mother. Hallo, Tina, I think we met briefly the other night.

Tina (*glaring at him*) Yes.

Poppy It's all right, Tina, I'm fine ...

Tina Sure?

Poppy Yes.

Tina goes back into the bedroom

I'm sorry. Shall we go downstairs? I'll pour you another drink. My husband shouldn't be much more than five minutes.

Benedict Well, quite frankly, Mrs McCracken, I don't think I can stay much longer myself ...

Poppy Oh, dear ...

Benedict I've one or two other evening commitments. I think I must be on my way.

Poppy Yes, of course. In that case, let me ... (*She indicates the stairs*)

Benedict I wonder, just before I go ... Your husband said it would be in order—if I could have the briefcase. To take with me.

Poppy Oh, no. I'm sorry. I was given to understand that——

Benedict I assure you, it is quite in order.

Poppy Yes. Well, the point is, he's taken it with him. Wherever he went. I'm sorry.

Benedict Oh dear, how inconvenient.

Poppy I am sorry. You'll have to wait till he comes back. With it.

Benedict I somehow feel that mightn't be in the best interests of my health.

Poppy I can put the fire on for you.

She tries to usher him downstairs again. Benedict seems reluctant to go

Benedict This is all very unfortunate. So it's not here?

Poppy Sorry.

Benedict You know something, Mrs McCracken. When I was a little boy, whenever I went to parties, we used to play a game called hunt the slipper. Have you ever played it yourself? I'm sure you have. Perhaps even with your own children? Well, of all the games there were, that was my favourite. Because I was really very, very good at it indeed.

Benedict begins to drive Poppy slowly backwards along the landing towards the near bedroom. She seems nearly hypnotized by Benedict

And do you know my secret? I'll tell you. I'd walk straight into the room where whatever it was had been hidden and I'd look straight at whoever I knew had hidden it and—try as they might, Mrs McCracken—they'd give themselves away. They just couldn't resist sliding their eyes round that little bit, to make sure it was still safely hidden. Rather the same as you yourself did just a moment ago, Mrs McCracken.

Poppy Listen, I don't know what you think you're doing——

They are now in the near bedroom

Benedict Now my guess is, that it's somewhere in here. (*He switches on the bedroom light*) Am I right?

Poppy Look, I'm afraid I must ask you to leave now, Mr Hough.

Benedict Just as soon as I find my property, Mrs McCracken, I shall be happily on my way.

Poppy (*louder*) I'm sorry, I refuse to be intimidated ...

Benedict Ssh! Mrs McCracken. We shall have to learn to play this game very quietly, shan't we? Otherwise we might frighten our grandchildren. And that would never do, would it?

Poppy (*starting to get indignant*) Now, you listen to me——

Benedict Sssh! (*He looks towards the cupboard*) What about in here?

He passes Poppy who instinctively draws away slightly. Benedict looks in the cupboard

Poppy My other daughter is here as well, you know. Just along there.

Benedict Who? Young Gladys? Well, we mustn't disturb her either, must we? (*Examining the cupboard*) No, nothing in here.

Poppy I think that was my husband's car.

Benedict If you were a sport, you'd shout out "warmer". Or "colder, colder" ... Ah, now where did I catch those lovely eyes looking then ... Eh? Under here perhaps?

He bends to look under the bed. From the other side Poppy grabs up the attaché case and runs for the door

No, no. That's cheating. Unfair ...

Poppy You can't have it ... Get away!

Poppy rushes into the bathroom and tries to close the door. Benedict, hot on her heels, prevents her doing so. Despite her efforts, he slowly manages to get the door open. He is evidently stronger than he looks

Benedict (*quietly*) Now, now. Naughty, naughty, naughty, Mrs McCracken.

Poppy (*struggling*) You keep out of here ...

Benedict (*as he slowly forces open the door*) When I used to go to parties little girls who cheated used to get smacked ... Are you a believer at all in corporal punishment, Mrs McCracken? I must admit I've invariably found it most effective. Especially for little girls who—cheat!

With a last shove he forces the door open. Poppy recoils and all but falls into the bath. Benedict switches on the light. Poppy stands, panting, clasping the attaché case to her

(*Advancing on her*) Come on, now ... come on ...
Poppy (*screaming*) Tina!
Benedict Oh, now that's really naughty. Smack! Smack! Smack!
Jack (*calling*) Come on, you lot. I want to get home and have my dinner.

Benedict grabs the attaché case and they wrestle semi-silently

Benedict (*struggling*) You didn't really think I was just going to sit there
waiting while he rounded up your whole family ... Come on. Let go ...
Poppy (*simultaneously, with him*) I'm not going to ... I won't ... you
won't ...

Tina, who has heard Poppy's cry, comes rushing along the landing

Tina Mum? Mum, what's happening?
Poppy Don't let him get it, Tina. Help me stop him ...
Tina (*pitching in to help*) You leave her alone. You let go of my mother ...
Benedict (*enjoying himself*) Now, now, now. Two against one. This won't
do, girls ...
Poppy Give it to me ...
Tina Give to her ... let go!
Benedict I warn you, ladies, I'm much stronger than I look. I don't want to
hurt you. But I may be forced to if you don't—Aaah!

The three topple over on to the floor with a cry

Now, this is becoming very undignified ... (*To Tina*) Ow, now. Mustn't
bite, must we?

*They struggle on the floor for a moment. Their combined strengths are more or
less equally matched. A deadlock. During this, Anita comes from the
dining-room*

Anita Sorry, Jack.
Jack Well? You come up with a solution?
Anita Yes, we have. But I'm afraid it's not one you'll like.
Jack (*sarcastically*) You mean, I've got to find the money myself?
Anita The only solution, as we see it, and we've talked it round and round,
is that we hand the original money over to Vincenzo in there and he'll get
his brother to do the rest. Arrange for Mr Hough to have a little accident.
Nothing dramatic.

Jack stares at her

Tina (*yelling*) Sammy! Sammy! For God's sake, come and help us!
Jack I don't think I can have heard you correctly ...
Poppy Sammy! She's got those bloody headphones on, I bet.
Jack Arrange an accident? You're actually talking about murdering him,
aren't you? That's what you're talking about?
Poppy ⎱
Tina ⎰ (*yelling in unison*) Sammy
Anita Jack, it's the only solution ...
Jack If that is the only solution, God help us ...

Anita If you don't want to see us all in prison . . .
Jack (*storming out through the hall*) That's it. That's it. We have reached the pit. We have touched the sewage. We are back on all fours. Not another word on the subject. Good-night.

Jack exits slamming the front door

Anita stands looking after him. Cliff comes out into the hall from the dining-room

Cliff I gather he didn't take it too well?
Anita Oh, he'll come round to it. You know Jack . . . Let's all have another drink, shall we?

She goes back into the dining-room with Cliff. Meanwhile, in the bathroom the fight continues

Benedict Come on now, girls, you've had your fun. That's enough. Or someone will get hurt . . .

With a huge effort he heaves the three of them off the floor for a second. They now teeter on the edge of the bath. The attaché case comes open at this point and the bathroom is filled with notes

Poppy (*alarmed*) Hold on, Tina.
Tina (*struggling*) I am, I am, I am . . .

Samantha comes out from her bedroom, rather blearily, her headphones still round her neck

Samantha Somebody call . . . ? (*Calling as she comes along the landing*) Mum? Mum?
Poppy Sammy, come and help us.
Tina (*with her*) Sammy!
Benedict (*still enjoying himself enormously*) Oh, not Gladys as well. This is getting very unfair . . .

Samantha enters the bathroom and surveys the scene in amazement

Samantha What are you doing?
Poppy Sammy, will you please help us . . .
Tina Sammy, for Christ's sake . . . he's trying to kill us.
Samantha Oh, it's you, is it? Sodding pukeface . . . (*She leaps in vigorously*) Right . . .
Benedict Hey! Hey! Gladys . . .

Under the weight of this latest assault, Benedict topples backwards into the bath and out of sight. There is a sharp cry and a terrible thud. Tina and Poppy cease the struggle. Poppy recoils holding the nearly empty briefcase. Tina slides back on to the floor exhausted. Samantha continues her onslaught

Poppy Sammy! Sammy! That'll do! That'll do!
Tina (*with a yell*) Sammy!

Samantha stops. Out of breath, she sits with the others on the floor. One gathers she was in a fairly dazed state when she started. A silence

(*Panting*) My God. Will you look at all this money?

Samantha Where's it come from?

Poppy It's your dad's ...

Samantha Did he nick it?

Poppy No. Not your dad. You should know better than that, Sammy.

Tina How is he? That man ...

Poppy I don't know, I'll ... (*She examines Benedict*) He doesn't seem to be breathing. (*She listens*) He's not breathing. (*Stunned*) He's dead.

Tina (*in an appalled whisper*) Oh, God.

Samantha Good.

Poppy Sammy! He's got this great cut in his head from somewhere, he's ... Look at all this blood. (*Appalled*) Oh, dear heaven, what's Jack going to say?

They all stay there in various attitudes of collapse, unable to move due to exhaustion and varying degrees of shock

Jack comes in the front door and closes it

The women react. Jack goes straight to the sitting-room

Tina (*softly*) It's Dad.

Jack (*seeing the sitting-room empty*) Poppy!

Poppy What's he going to say ...

Jack (*glancing into the empty kitchen*) Poppy! (*He grows slightly more alarmed*)

Tina (*indicating Benedict*) Perhaps we can hide him somewhere ...

Poppy No, he'll have to know. Your dad will have to be told.

Jack (*at the foot of the stairs, calling*) Poppy! Tina!

Poppy (*calling back feebly*) We're up here, Jack ...

Jack (*starting up the stairs*) What?

Tina In here, Dad ...

Jack reaches the landing, uncertain as to where to locate them. He looks in the near bedroom, then the bathroom. He stops short, startled, as he sees the state of the three women

Poppy Hallo, Jack ...

Tina Hallo, Dad.

Samantha Hi ...

Jack What are you doing? What are you all doing in here?

Poppy We were——

Jack What are you doing with all that money? What the hell's been going on?

Poppy We were trying to save it for you, Jack ...

Jack And where's Mr Hough, then?

Poppy He's——

Samantha He's in the bath.

Jack What?

Poppy (*pointing; almost inaudible*) In the bath.

Jack steps over them to see for himself

Jack Oh, shit. (*He stares at Benedict*) Oh, shit. Poppy, what have you done? (*After a pause*) Oh, shit.

Poppy (*very penitent*) I'm very sorry, Jack.

Jack Oh. (*He sways*) I'm a bit dizzy ...

Poppy Don't faint, love, don't faint in here ...

Tina Steady, Dad ...

Poppy He faints at blood ...

Jack No, it's all right. I'm all right. (*Recovering*) What are we going to do ...?

Poppy (*smiling feebly*) At least he's in the bath. Not so much of a mess ...

Jack (*dully*) Good thinking, Poppy, yes.

This strikes Poppy as funny. She laughs. First Tina, then Samantha follow suit. They scream with laughter. Jack stares at them—incredulously

All right. That'll do. That'll do. THAT'LL DO!

They stop. A silence

Blimey O'Reilly. It's like the bloody Borgias' bathroom in here. What's the matter with you all?

Poppy (*the tears coming now*) What are we going to do, Jack ...?

Tina (*starting to cry, too*) What are we going to do, Dad?

Jack (*stronger at once*) It's all right. It's all right. We'll sort it out ...

Poppy (*weeping*) I'm terribly sorry ...

Tina (*weeping*) It wasn't your fault, Mum.

Samantha seems to have gone into mild shock

Jack Now, it's all right. It's all right. Now, come on. Let's get organized. Tina, you see to Kevin, it sounds as if he's calling for you. Sammy, I want you to pick all this lot up. Every penny, do you hear ...

Samantha Oh, Dad. Why's it always me?

Poppy (*between tears*) What about ... what about him?

Jack Leave him just as he is, I'll deal with that. Sammy, draw the curtain round him, there's a girl.

Samantha draws the shower curtain and then begins to pick up the notes under the next. She then goes to her bedroom

Tina returns to the far bedroom

Jack leads Poppy from the bathroom and downstairs

And you're coming downstairs with me, all right?

Poppy (*sniffing*) Yes ...

Jack (*gently*) You know what we're going to do?

Poppy (*faintly*) No ...

Jack (*as to a child*) We're going to get things cleared up and then we're going to put all this lot behind us, you see? Anita's got some friends who'll get rid of him. Him in the bath ... they'll know how to do that, they're used to that ...

Poppy Are they?

Jack Oh yes, they do that sort of thing in their sleep. And do you know what the day after tomorrow is?

Poppy No.

Jack It's your dad's birthday, isn't it?

Poppy Oh, yes, I'd forgotten . . .

Jack Well, we mustn't forget that, must we? We've got to give old Ken a real treat, haven't we? For his seventy-fifth? Us and all the family? Eh?

Poppy (*smiling bravely*) We will . . .

Jack We'll have a real party. Des and Harriet and Anita and Cliff and Roy and Tina . . .

He is swamped by the next. As Jack speaks, the events start to occur. Slowly the scene transforms as people gather for the party. Music also starts from the hi-fi, as before. Cliff, Roy and Desmond come out of the dining-room. Desmond carries a plate from the cold buffet. He goes into the near sitting-room. Roy goes into the far sitting-room. Cliff remains in the hall. Through the front door, into the hall, come Anita, Harriet and Lotario, 32, a smartly dressed, sharp-featured man, looking very much like a representative of an organized crime syndicate. They are all talking together

Anita This is Lotario Rivetti . . . this is my—I don't know what to call her, really . . . she's my brother-in-law's wife's brother's wife . . . does that make any sense?

Lotario (*who speaks perfect English*) I think so. I think so. We have similar family complications in my country, as you can well imagine . . .

Harriet (*who seems to be making a slight effort*) Yes, I can see you might . . .

Anita We're going to get something to eat. Are you going to join us, Harriet?

Harriet No, I won't. Not just at the moment . . .

The last is played under the following

Cliff (*as he comes out of the dining-room*) Poppy, my darling—(*kissing her*)—you have excelled yourself yet again. That spread is sumptuous. Is that the right word—sumptuous?

Poppy Thank you . . .

Cliff Is that not so, Des?

Desmond Oh, yes indeed.

Cliff There you are. There speaks the expert.

Jack No higher praise . . .

Poppy Well, thank you. Excuse me, just one second . . .

Poppy goes into the dining-room

Cliff You got a drink, Jack? Can I get you one?

Jack Ta, yes. Large scotch and water.

Cliff Right.

Cliff goes into the far sitting-room. Harriet goes into the near sitting-room as Anita and Lotario head towards the dining-room. They meet up with Jack. Desmond comes into the hall

Desmond Jack, is it possible to have a quick word . . . ?

Jack Could it wait a second, Des? I need to freshen up.
Desmond It'll only——
Anita Jack. You haven't met Lotario, have you? Lotario, this is my brother-in-law, Jack McCracken.
Jack (*slowly and loudly*) Hallo. Welcome to our party. *Ciao.*
Lotario Hallo. It's a splendid do. Absolutely wonderful. I was just telling Anita, it reminds me very much of our own family parties back in Milan.
Jack (*startled*) Ah.
Anita This is the one that speaks English.
Jack Yes. I noticed.
Lotario Yes. I was very fortunate. I was educated privately in Dorset ...
Jack Great.
Anita (*dragging Lotario away*) Come on. We're going to get something to eat ...
Lotario Talk to you later on, old boy.
Jack Yes, rather. You betcha.

Anita and Lotario go into the dining-room. Jack goes upstairs before Desmond can grab him. Cliff comes out of the far sitting-room with a drink for Jack

Desmond (*vainly, after Jack*) Jack ... (*Seeing Cliff*) Cliff, could I have a quick word?
Cliff Yes, right you are, Des. I've just got to give Jack his drink ...

Desmond ignores this and draws Cliff to one side. Upstairs, Jack has gone into the near bedroom and starts to change his shirt, as before

Desmond It's just—I need Jack's OK to—you know—move off. You know. Leave the country. Set my overseas interests in motion. Only I don't want to do anything to jeopardize things, Cliff. Or the business, obviously.
Cliff You're going to have to wait a bit, Des.
Desmond Yes but, Cliff, you must appreciate the situation between me and Harriet is increasingly ... you know how things are ...
Cliff You are going to have to be patient, old son. Grin and bear her for a bit longer. We can't have you doing a bunk now. It'd look all wrong, Des. First Mr Hough, then you. We can't have everyone disappearing. Hasn't she been a bit more reasonable lately? I thought Anita'd had a word with her ...
Desmond Oh yes, she's been much better. That certainly helped—I was grateful to Anita for that, Cliff. I don't know what she said but ...

Cliff has now started up the stairs with Jack's drink

Tina comes out of the dining-room

Desmond goes, rather unhappily, into the near sitting-room

Tina I'll get some more. Where are they? In the drawer?

Tina goes into the kitchen

Desmond (*to Harriet*) You going to have something to eat, dear?
Harriet (*wincing*) Certainly not.

Desmond Are you sure? It's really delicious. There are things there you'd like. There's a nice trifle. You like trifle, don't you?

Harriet Desmond, please leave me alone. Go away.

Desmond I was only trying to ...

Rather dejectedly, Desmond goes into the far sitting-room, leaving Harriet alone. Tina finds the forks and passes them through the hatch

Tina Here we are, Mum ...

Poppy (*from the dining-room*) Oh, thank you, dear.

Tina returns to the dining-room. Under the next, Anita and Lotario cross from the dining-room to the near sitting-room with plates of food. Cliff arrives in Jack's bedroom

Cliff (*presenting the drink*) There you go.

Jack Shut the door.

Cliff (*doing so*) The Italians are proving a bit difficult ...

Jack Never mind them. What about Harriet? Is she safe now?

Cliff Yes, she's all right. For the time being ...

Jack I mean, if she gets wind of all this from Des and goes blabbing off to Yvonne again, we're back to square one, aren't we? In spades.

Cliff Harriet's all right. Anita's talked to her.

Jack I hope she talked her round.

Jack goes out of the near bedroom and into the bathroom to rinse his face. Cliff follows him. Anita and Lotario enter the sitting-room from the hall

Anita Where did we put our drinks then?

Lotario I think they're through here ... (*He leads the way through to the far sitting-room*)

Anita Oh, yes. So they are. Hallo, Harriet. All alone?

Harriet I'm all right.

Anita (*smiling*) Good.

Anita goes through to the far sitting-room. Jack and Cliff are now both in the bathroom

Jack Shut the door.

Cliff does so

What's the matter with the Italians, then?

Cliff They're proving a bit expensive, Jack, that's all. I mean their bill for the removal and disposal of our friend is costing an arm and a leg, if you'll pardon the expression.

Jack How much?

Cliff Fifty.

Jack That's blackmail, that is.

Cliff I know. But we weren't in much of a position to argue, Jack. And, I mean, with the Rivettis you got all the equipment, the van, the boat. They probably even had the proper lead weights.

Jack Right. So where's that leave us? Overdrawn, doesn't it?

Cliff Well, I took the liberty, Jack. I took the liberty of doing a deal in kind.

Jack What deal?

Cliff It appears they could find a use for our own domestic furniture distribution network for the circulation of urgent medical supplies.

Jack Urgent medical supplies? What are we talking about here? Are we talking about drugs?

Cliff No, medical supplies.

Jack Don't try telling me the Rivettis have joined the International Red Cross. They mean drugs. No way.

Cliff Now, Jack——

Jack Forget it.

Cliff Jack. I know it's a dirty, filthy, stinking business——

Jack Right.

Cliff And normally, I would say no, with you. Categorically no. But these are what they term urgent medical supplies. Meaning they are only intended—and I have their solemn vow on that—they are only intended for established users who, if denied their regular supply—well, it would entail a great deal of unnecessary suffering . . .

Jack No, I'm sorry, I——

Cliff Yes, I know it's a dirty, filthy, stinking, lousy, disgusting business, Jack—but we do have a solemn undertaking that there will be no first-time users involved here, Jack. Otherwise, I would say no with you. No, no and again categorically no.

Jack We have that undertaking?

Cliff We do.

Jack Well. This is just a one-off, you understand. You tell them I'm not doing this on a regular basis. It's only till we've paid them off.

Cliff Absolutely. Yes . . .

Jack starts to leave the bathroom

There should be quite a bit in it for us as well, incidentally. But that's only incidental. (*He turns off the bathroom light*)

They both return to the bedroom where Jack puts on his clean shirt. Anita comes in briefly to the near sitting-room

Anita Come on, Harriet, come and keep Desmond company. He's all on his own, poor man . . .

Harriet (*drily*) Oh, dear . . .

Anita (*pleasantly enough*) Now, Harriet. Remember our talk? You must look after Desmond, otherwise he'll start finding new friends, won't he? And before you know it, these new friends of his, they'll be round at your house at all hours of the day and night, leaving doors open, so that Peggy could so easily run straight out into that busy main road. Straight under the wheels of some great big lorry . . .

Harriet has risen during the last of this and hurries into the far sitting-room

(*Cheerfully*) Here she is . . . (*She goes back after her*)

Jack Anything else?

Cliff No, that's it for now ...
Jack Right. Well done.

Cliff makes to leave the bedroom

Incidentally, Cliff—close the door, will you—I think, in due course, I'd like you and Anita to consider coming on to the board ...
Cliff Oh. What, you mean——?
Jack As full directors. To join me and Desmond. With a view to taking over from him later when he leaves.
Cliff I hope he won't be leaving us for a good bit yet, Jack.
Jack Well, frankly, he's worse than useless, Cliff. The sooner he starts polluting the Mediterranean with burnt cooking fat, the better.
Cliff No. Still, we'd all prefer to have him around just the same, wouldn't we? Where we can see him? I mean, you're the guv'nor, Jack, but it seems to me we're the sort of family that needs to stick together ...
Jack (*rather moved*) You're dead right, Cliff. (*Embracing him*) We're a family, for God's sake.
Cliff (*rather bemused by the force of this reaction*) True. See you down there then, Jack.

Cliff goes out and along the landing. As he does so ...

Samantha, in her party outfit, comes along the landing from her bedroom

Hello, Sammy. How are you doing?
Samantha Hallo, Uncle Cliff.
Cliff Coming to join the knees-up?
Samantha (*staring at him blankly*) What?
Cliff (*studying her for a second*) Right, I'll see you down there ...

Cliff goes downstairs. Poppy hurries from the dining-room. She is dressed in her boldest party dress yet. This one obviously was bought for her, not for Anita

Poppy (*calling upstairs*) Jack? (*To Cliff*) Is Jack coming down?
Cliff On his way.
Poppy I think they're here ...

Poppy hovers in the hall. Cliff goes to the far sitting-room. Jack finishes dressing in the bedroom and meets Samantha as he sets off downstairs

Jack Hallo, Sammy. All right, then?
Samantha I'm all right.
Jack Right. (*After a pause*) Good. See you downstairs. (*He hurries downstairs*)
Samantha See you downstairs. (*During the next, she stands for a time at the top of the stairs, and then, as if unable to face the throng below, goes into the darkened bathroom where she sits for the remainder of the play, staring ahead of her blankly*
Jack (*reaching the hall*) Now then. Where is everyone?

Poppy Oh, there you are. Quickly. He's arrived . . . he's just driven up with Yvonne in the taxi.
Jack Oh, good. Just in time.

Jack goes into the far sitting-room and shoos people through to the near one. They turn off the lights as before

Jack Come on, everyone, Ken's arrived.
Poppy (*waving Tina out of the dining-room*) Come on, Tina. Quickly.

Tina scurries across the hall and into the near sitting-room where she joins Cliff, Anita, Lotario, Harriet, Desmond, Roy and Jack. Poppy hovers in the hall, waiting

Anita (*as someone touches her*) Oooh!
All Sssh!
Anita Here we go again . . .

The doorbell rings. Poppy opens the door immediately

Ken and Yvonne enter. Ken is much the same, perhaps a little vaguer. Yvonne is like a Christmas tree. She sparkles with expensive jewellery, everywhere

Poppy Hallo, there. Come in, come in.
Ken Hallo, my flower. Hallo, my dearest.
Poppy Let me take your coats.
Yvonne (*winking*) Are we the first?
Poppy I think you are, yes.
Ken Happy birthday, my dear. And very many more.
Yvonne No, it's your birthday, Ken. It's yours. (*To Poppy*) He keeps forgetting. He kept wishing the taxi driver many happy returns.
Ken Mine? Is it my birthday, then?
Poppy Yes, it's yours. Not mine.
Ken I know that, girl. Seventy-five. Seventy-five today. Right?
Poppy That's right. Now you come on through.
Ken This is very nice. Who lives here, then?

Poppy leads them across the hall. As Ken enters the near sitting-room, the lights are switched on. A great cry from everyone and they all sing "Happy Birthday". At the end, applause. People cluster around Ken with good wishes. He seems quite overwhelmed. Poppy draws Jack to one side.

Poppy Jack! Have you seen what that woman's wearing? Have you seen what Yvonne's wearing?
Jack What's that?
Poppy That's all Grace's jewellery. Those are my mother's diamonds she's got on.
Jack Perhaps Ken lent them to her.
Poppy (*with some venom*) Nonsense. Jack, she's stolen them. If they belong to anyone, they're mine. That woman has stolen them and she thinks we daren't do anything about it. Little thieving bitch . . .

Jack It's all right, love. If she has stolen them, then she'll answer for it. I'm having no more of that, ever again. From now on this family's going to be subject to a few hard and fast rules. And anyone who breaks them is going to have the family to answer to. I'll get Anita to have a word with her later. Now come on, stop worrying and enjoy the party . . .

Poppy (*lovingly*) You're a good man, Jack. You're such a good man.

She kisses him lovingly. They both return to the throng

Ken (*above the chatter*) Ladies and . . . ladies . . .

Cliff Speech! Speech!

Anita Ssshh! Quiet!

A silence. Ken and Yvonne have both been given drinks

Ken Ladies and Gentlemen . . . I just want to say . . . now, I'm not saying very much. Because it's not my place to. It's not my day. All I want to say is . . . Jack. (*He looks towards Desmond*)

Desmond (*pointing gently*) That's Jack, Dad . . .

Ken Yes, it's Jack I'm talking to, not you, you fool. (*Turning to Jack*) Jack. Thank you, for everything. And you know what I mean by everything. And happy birthday, son.

He raises his glass. Everyone, rather startled, toasts Jack

Jack Well. This is an unexpected anniversary pleasure. (*He reflects*) I've made my speech for this year. It still stands. I'd simply like to propose this toast. Here's to you, Ken. Here's to us. Here's to the family. And finally, here's to the business. We've had our share of troubles and we've seen them off. And together, I can promise you this, we will continue to see them all off—whoever they are and wherever they come from. Ladies and Gentlemen, I give you—the family business!

All The family business!

As they drink, the Lights fade on the party guests—leaving, for a few seconds or so, the image of Samantha, huddled and alone. Then, as we lose her too, Black-out

CURTAIN

FURNITURE AND PROPERTY LIST

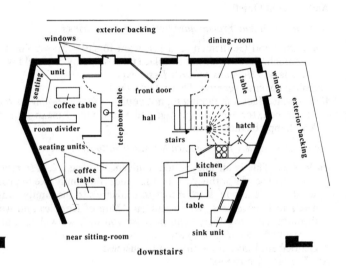

exterior backing

windows

dining-room

unit

seating

table

window

coffee table

front door

room divider

telephone table

hall

exterior backing

seating units

stairs

hatch

coffee table

kitchen units

table

table

sink unit

near sitting-room

downstairs

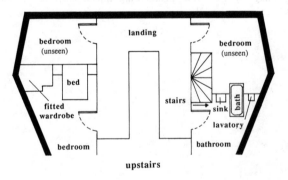

landing

bedroom (unseen)

bedroom (unseen)

bed

stairs

bath

fitted wardrobe

sink

lavatory

bedroom

bathroom

upstairs

ACT I

On stage: *Downstairs*

> *Sitting-room*:
> Seating units
> Coffee tables. *On them:* ashtrays
> TV
> Shelving fitments
> Room divider. *On it:* bowls of crisps, nuts, olives, etc., telephone, hi-fi,
>   records, bottles of drink, glasses, ice-bucket, tray, another tray with
>   bottle of malt whisky and 3 glasses for **Cliff** on page 40
> Carpet
> Table lamps
> Book, personal stereo, glass of Coke for **Samantha**
> Drinks for **Ken, Desmond, Harriet, Yvonne, Cliff, Anita, Uberto, Tina, Roy**

> *Hall:*
> Table. *On it:* telephone
> Cupboard. *In it:* coats for **Anita, Uberto, Yvonne, Ken, Harriet, Cliff,
>   Desmond**

> *Kitchen:*
> Kitchen units. *In drawer:* tablespoon. *On shelves:* cookery books
> Cooker
> Sink unit with practical taps. *Near it:* tea-towel on hook
> Table
> Stools
> Fridge. *In it:* plates of fake food covered with foil (including one real piece
>   of food for **Desmond** on page 15), tin of Coke. *In freezer compartment:*
>   tray of ice-cubes
> Pedal bin
> Telephone
> Kitchen towel on holder
> Key in back door
> Hatch to dining-room (table and chairs visible through it)

> *Upstairs*

> *Bedroom:*
> Double bed with bedding
> Bedside drawers. *On one:* telephone
> Shelving fitments. *In one drawer:* shirts for **Jack**
> Fitted wardrobes with sliding door. *In them:* tie rack with ties, suits,
>   dresses
> Clothes basket

> *Bathroom:*
> Bath with practical taps and practical shower, shower curtain
> Lavatory
> Basin with practical taps. *Above it:* mirror
> Towel rail with towel
> Stool

Off stage: Armful of washing with Y-fronts on top **(Poppy)**
> Sheet, Giorgo's shirt **(Anita)**

Shoes, socks **(Giorgio)**
Plastic bucket from pedal bin **(Desmond)**

Personal: **Benedict:** small notebook, calling card
Yvonne: brooch for entrance on page 30

ACT II

Kitchen:

Strike: Plastic bucket

Set: Phone back on hook
Blackened, smoking casserole in oven
Portable cassette player (practical) with "Teach Yourself Spanish" cassette playing, oven gloves on table
Tea-towels, creased prospectus for holiday village in drawer
Cashbook with bonds, bank statements, etc. concealed under oven
Forks in drawer
Tray of ice-cubes in freezer compartment in fridge
Back door locked

Bedroom:

Set: Dresses strewn around (including **Poppy**'s own dress)
Box of jewellery (including brooch, necklace, ear-rings) in bedside drawer
Poppy's handbag

Sitting-room:

Strike: Bowls of crisps, nuts, olives, etc.
Tray with bottle of malt whisky, dirty glasses

Set: Enclosed dog basket
Empty ice-bucket on room divider
Drinks for cast for party at end

Off stage: 2 of Anita's dresses **(Poppy)**
Children's book **(Tina)**
CD player with plug dangling, wrapped in old sheet **(Samantha)**
Empty glass **(Tina)**
Attaché case containing bundles of £10 notes **(Jack)**
Heavy spanner **(Cliff)**
Plates of food **(Cliff, Desmond)**
Plates of food **(Anita, Lotario)**

Personal: **Anita:** gold bracelet, wrist-watch
Cliff: doorkey
Orlando: wallet with family photographs
Jack: attaché case key, wrist-watch
Benedict: notebook, wrist-watch, blood sac
Vincenzo: spectacles
Samantha: headphones round neck (page 78)
Yvonne: jewellery

LIGHTING PLOT

Practical fittings required: table lamps in sitting-room, overhead lights in all rooms

Interior. A sitting-room, kitchen, hall, landing, bathroom and bedroom

ACT I

To open: Evening: lighting on all downstairs areas and landing, table lamps on

Cue 1	Guests switch off table lamps *Snap off each lamp in turn*	(Page 2)
Cue 2	**Poppy** switches off overhead light in sitting-room *Snap off overhead lights in sitting-room*	(Page 2)
Cue 3	**Jack** switches on overhead lights in sitting-room *Snap up overhead lights*	(Page 4)
Cue 4	As guests switch on table lamps *Snap up each lamp in turn*	(Page 5)
Cue 5	**Jack** goes into bedroom and switches on light *Snap up light in bedroom*	(Page 9)
Cue 6	**Jack** goes into bathroom and switches on light *Snap up light in bathroom*	(Page 11)
Cue 7	**Poppy** and **Tina** go into Samantha's room *Change to late afternoon lighting on all areas*	(Page 27)
Cue 8	**Ken** leaves the bathroom and goes off into one of the far bedrooms *Change to evening lighting—sitting-room, kitchen, hall and landing*	(Page 31)
Cue 9	**Poppy** exits *Lights change—hall and landing lights only*	(Page 35)
Cue 10	**Jack** switches on kitchen light *Snap up kitchen light*	(Page 36)
Cue 11	**Jack** switches off kitchen light *Snap off kitchen light*	(Page 36)
Cue 12	**Jack** switches on sitting-room light *Snap up sitting-room light*	(Page 36)
Cue 13	Telephone rings in kitchen *Bring up lights in kitchen*	(Page 42)
Cue 14	**Harriet** cringes, **Desmond** steels himself, **Cliff** listens and the dog yaps on *Black-out*	(Page 43)

ACT II

To open: Afternoon lighting on all areas

Cue 15	**Desmond:** "Harriet . . . ?" *Change to evening lighting on all areas except sitting-room, bathroom and bedroom*	(Page 58)
Cue 16	**Poppy** switches on overhead light and table lamps in sitting-room *Snap up overhead light and table lamps in turn*	(Page 60)
Cue 17	**Poppy** switches off kitchen light *Snap off kitchen light*	(Page 62)
Cue 18	**Desmond** enters kitchen and switches on light *Snap up kitchen light*	(Page 68)
Cue 19	**Poppy** enters bedroom *Snap up bedroom light*	(Page 70)
Cue 20	**Poppy** leaves the bedroom *Snap off bedroom light*	(Page 70)
Cue 21	**Anita** limps and hops into bedroom *Snap up bedroom light*	(Page 71)
Cue 22	**Anita** leaves bedroom *Snap off bedroom light*	(Page 71)
Cue 23	**Benedict** switches on bathroom light *Snap up bathroom light*	(Page 73)
Cue 24	**Benedict** switches off bathroom light *Snap off bathroom light*	(Page 73)
Cue 25	**Benedict** switches on bedroom light *Snap up bedroom light*	(Page 74)
Cue 26	**Benedict** switches off bedroom light *Snap off bedroom light*	(Page 74)
Cue 27	**Benedict** switches on bedroom light *Snap up bedroom light*	(Page 76)
Cue 28	**Benedict** switches on bathroom light *Snap up bathroom light*	(Page 76)
Cue 29	**Cliff** switches off bathroom light *Snap off bathroom light*	(Page 84)
Cue 30	As **Jack** etc. switch off lights in sitting-room *Snap off overhead light and table lamps in turn*	(Page 86)
Cue 31	As **Ken** enters the near sitting-room *Snap up lights in sitting-room*	(Page 86)
Cue 32	**All:** "The family business!" *They drink* *Fade lights on party guests, leaving image of* **Samantha**, *huddled and alone, for a few seconds, then black-out*	(Page 87)

EFFECTS PLOT

ACT I

ACT II

MADE AND PRINTED IN GREAT BRITAIN BY
LATIMER TREND & COMPANY LTD PLYMOUTH

MADE IN ENGLAND